AN INTRODUCTORY GUIDE TO
FLOW MEASUREMENT

An Introductory Guide to Flow Measurement

ROGER C. BAKER

Professor of Fluid Engineering
Cranfield Institute of Technology

Mechanical Engineering Publications Limited, London

© Roger C. Baker 1989

ISBN 0 85298 670 X

British Library Cataloguing in Publication Data

Baker, R.C. (Roger Cecil), *1939–*
Introductory guide to flow measurement.
1. Fluids. Flow. Measurement
I. Title
532'.053
ISBN 0-85298-670-X

Printed in Great Britain at the Alden Press, Oxford

Contents

Contents

PREFACE

This book is aimed at the busy practising engineer, who is faced with a flow measurement problem and requires enough information to enable him to assess the advice he receives from manufacturers, and to make his own contribution to discussion with experts.

It is not possible in a book of this length to cover such a wide ranging subject to any great depth or thoroughness. The author has attempted to select information which will allow the reader to understand the essential background technology, to obtain the essentials of the flowmeter operating principles, to have some guide as to the likely performance of a particular instrument, and to weigh up the advantages and disadvantages.

This book is about existing flowmeters, their operation, installation, and application advantages and disadvantages. As such it is mainly concerned with the mechanical and fluid mechanical aspects. The output signal, if electrical, is either a 4–20 mA signal, a frequency signal, or other standard. Most manufacturers will offer a standard range of output electrical signals.

The style of the book, in which the key points are emphasized by shading, again has the objective of enabling the reader to find essential information as quickly as possible. The style, and the material in the book, stem from the author's lectures to industrial personnel on Cranfield's intensive short course programme. The lectures, like the book, aim to transmit as much information as efficiently as possible in a short time.

Chapter 3, Selection, is arguably the most important chapter. The main considerations are listed, and the flowmeter types are tabulated with operating ranges and likely performances. From this table the reader may wish to turn to the sections of most immediate interest. Chapters 1 and 2 set the background in terms of precision, flow behaviour, fluid parameters, and calibration techniques. Chapters 4–7 review as many designs and techniques as possible within the scope of this short book, and Chapter 8 looks to further developments.

I have attempted to provide a fair and correct description and assessment of each flowmeter type and its limitations. However, it should be recognised that some instruments may out-perform the guidelines and others may fail to meet them. The reader should therefore accept the values given with caution and seek further advice when necessary.

The dominant reflection, having completed this book, is that almost every statement needs much more qualification than it is possible to give, and every attempt to generalize is dangerous. Therefore, reader, do not proceed uncritically, and if you find this book useful, but can suggest corrections and improvements, the author will be pleased to hear from you.

Roger C. Baker

St Albans, October 1988

ACKNOWLEDGEMENTS

In writing this book I have been particularly conscious of the debt which I owe to many colleagues and students from whom I have learned. I have also been privileged to listen to many lecturers on the Cranfield Short Course programme, who have spoken from wide experience of flow measurement technology, and I have benefitted from those who have written the many books and articles on the subject. Within the brief scope of this book it is not possible to give due credit for all the points covered, and indeed my interpretation and summary of many ideas may not do justice to each individually. However, some I must acknowledge: my past and present colleagues at Cranfield, who have specialised in flow measurement, particularly John Hemp, Michael Sanderson, Richard Furness, and Jane Heritage; Alan Hayward for his excellent and concise book on flow measurement, and Dick Miller for his exhaustive handbook on the subject, from both of which I have learned; Cranfield/NEL Calibration Short Course which I attended at a critical stage of proof correction, and in which Frank Kinghorn's contributions particularly helped me to clarify my ideas. I am very grateful to Terry Cousins and Simon McCandlish who read the manuscript and gave helpful suggestions; Brenda Hampshaw and Janet Dare who typed much of the manuscript; and Michael Spencer who edited the book and was very patient in handling my particular requests and my many proof changes. Finally, I am very grateful to my family who have put up with me working on the manuscript during family time at home, and to whom the book is dedicated.

to Liz, Sarah, Mark, John, and Rachel

NOMENCLATURE

A	Area of duct, area of target, constant
B	Bias; magnetic flux density
C	Influence coefficient; coefficient of discharge
C^*	Gas constant for sonic nozzle
C_{b-b}	Bend–bend loss coefficient correction
C_D	Sensitivity coefficient for dimensional changes
C_p	Specific heat at constant pressure
C_T	Sensitivity coefficient for temperature
c	Sound speed
D	Pipe diameter
d	Orifice or throat diameter; bluff body dimension
E	$\sqrt{\{1/(1-\beta^4)\}}$
f	Frequency
g	Gravitational acceleration
h, H	Height/head
K	Loss coefficients; pulses/unit volume; constants
k	Compressibility for a liquid, constant
L	Aerofoil lift; bend spacing; length of leakage gap in PD meter
l	Length of pipe; length of PD meter rotor; axial beam spacing
M	Molecular weight
m	Area ratio of throat to pipe
N	Rotational speed; number of blades
n	Number of measurements
p	Pressure
Q	Flowrate (actual); Q' flowmeter reading; Q'' flowmeter reading affected by changes from datum
q_v	Volume flowrate
q_m	Mass flowrate
q	Leakage volumetric flow; volumetric flowrate of injected tracer; heat transfer
Re	Reynolds number
R	Pipe radius; gas constant; wheel radius
$\bar{R}$	Universal gas constant
r	Radius

S	Experimental standard deviation; strouhal number; sensitivity of electromagnetic flowmeter
s	Spring constant
T	Temperature; torque
t	Student's t value; leakage gap clearance; time
U	Uncertainty; leakage clearance velocity in PD meter
$U V$	Velocity
ΔU	Potential difference between electrodes
V	Voltage; volume of a pipe between sampling points
v	Specific volume; volume of injected water with tracer
V_C	Centre line velocity
$\bar{V}$	Mean velocity
X	Angular momentum
x_i	Measurement value
$\bar{x}$	Mean value of measurements
y	Distance from duct wall

Greek symbols

α, β	Thermal coefficient of expansion
β	d/D; blade angle
γ	Ratio of specific heats
δ	Calibration correction; region lost by PD meter vanes
ε	Expansibility factor
ρ	Fluid density
ρ_1	Fluid density of upstream pressure tapping for differential pressure meters
μ	Dynamic viscosity
ν	Kinematic viscosity
τ	Shear stress; time period
ω	Rotational speed

CHAPTER 1

Introduction

flow
METER
SELECTION.

DO YOU NEED A FLOWMETER?
Volumetric or Mass Flow Measurement
  – which do you need?
How precise?
  – precision costs money
Maintenance
  – can you afford it?
Specification
  – have you obtained the complete specification?

Before you install a flowmeter, ask why you are doing so. Do you *really* need a flowmeter? Some years ago I was working on a flowmeter design to monitor flows in a very sensitive installation. Because flowmeter failure was unacceptable and two flowmeters could contradict, three flowmeters were proposed for each flowmeter position, and then four. At this stage it was considered that the monitoring might be done better with thermometers rather than flowmeters!

Do you need to measure the volumetric flow of the fluid ('fluid' will be used to mean either liquid or gas) or do you require the mass flow? In this book flowmeters are subdivided into momentum, volume, and mass. The flowmeters which respond to momentum are density dependent and a knowledge of density will be required to obtain either volume or mass flow.

If you do indeed need a flowmeter, how precise does it need to be? Precision costs money, not only in the initial cost of the instrument and an adequate installation, but in the maintenance of the required precision. If the installation will not allow adequate maintenance, or if flowmeter maintenance is likely to be the first casualty of financial economies, it is important to question the advisability of installing the instrument in the first place. It may also be worth considering whether another instrument measuring a quite different parameter would give an indication of plant behaviour adequately.

Virtually all flowmeters are available with standard electrical output. Where necessary manufacturers will provide special options. A few types have predominantly a mechanical read-out. However, it seems likely that we are on the threshold of major advances in signal processing and interpretation.

In the next few paragraphs it will be useful to look, first at the meaning of precision, and then at some of the factors, fluid mechanical and others, which affect the installed precision of a flow meter.

One very basic problem needs clarification first. Flows are measured in many and varied units, both of volumetric flow rate and of velocity in a certain pipe size. The conversions are often confusing and the table below gives a comparison of unit values, starting with the one used in the text, m^3/h, and giving (to two significant figures) other values. A conversion to mass flow in terms of water density is given at the foot of the table. Particular care is needed in specifying gas flows where temperature and pressure affect volumetric flow.

1.1 PRECISION

ACCURACY
  – the truthfulness of an instrument.
REPEATABILITY
  – the closeness of the agreement between successive measurements under constant conditions.
REPRODUCIBILITY
  – the closeness between measurements by an instrument when conditions have been changed.
UNCERTAINTY
  – the quality of the measurement.
CONFIDENCE LEVEL
  – the probability of the reading falling within certain limits.
LINEARITY
  – the closeness to a linear response.
RANGE
  – the maximum and minimum flowrates for which the uncertainty, linearity, etc. are applicable.
TURNDOWN RATIO
  – the ratio of maximum to minimum flowrate range values.
NOTE. In this book uncertainty will be given as a percentage of actual flowrate for a 95 per cent confidence level; and the tolerance will be given as a percentage of flowrate, unless otherwise stated.

There is much confusion about the various terms used to indicate the

	m^3/h*	l/min	Imp. gal/min	US gal/min	ft^3/min	Mean velocity (m/s) in a circular pipe of diameter:							
						10 mm	25 mm	50 mm	100 mm	200 mm	500 mm	1000 mm	2000 mm
Very low	10^{-3}	0·017	$3{\cdot}7 \times 10^{-3}$	$4{\cdot}4 \times 10^{-3}$	$5{\cdot}9 \times 10^{-4}$	$3{\cdot}5 \times 10^{-3}$	$5{\cdot}7 \times 10^{-4}$	$1{\cdot}4 \times 10^{-4}$	$3{\cdot}5 \times 10^{-5}$				
	10^{-2}	0·17	$3{\cdot}7 \times 10^{-2}$	$4{\cdot}4 \times 10^{-2}$	$5{\cdot}9 \times 10^{-3}$	$3{\cdot}5 \times 10^{-2}$	$5{\cdot}7 \times 10^{-3}$	$1{\cdot}4 \times 10^{-3}$	$3{\cdot}5 \times 10^{-4}$	$8{\cdot}8 \times 10^{-5}$	$1{\cdot}4 \times 10^{-5}$		
	0·1	1·7	0·37	0·44	$5{\cdot}9 \times 10^{-2}$	0·35	$5{\cdot}7 \times 10^{-2}$	$1{\cdot}4 \times 10^{-2}$	$3{\cdot}5 \times 10^{-3}$	$8{\cdot}8 \times 10^{-4}$	$1{\cdot}4 \times 10^{-4}$	$3{\cdot}5 \times 10^{-5}$	
	1	17	3·7	4·4	0·59	3·5	0·57	0·14	$3{\cdot}5 \times 10^{-2}$	$8{\cdot}8 \times 10^{-3}$	$1{\cdot}4 \times 10^{-3}$	$3{\cdot}5 \times 10^{-4}$	$8{\cdot}8 \times 10^{-5}$
	10	170	37	44	5·9	35	5·7	1·4	0·35	$8{\cdot}8 \times 10^{-2}$	$1{\cdot}4 \times 10^{-2}$	$3{\cdot}5 \times 10^{-3}$	$8{\cdot}8 \times 10^{-4}$
	100	1700	370	440	59	350	57	14	3·5	0·88	0·14	$3{\cdot}5 \times 10^{-2}$	$8{\cdot}8 \times 10^{-3}$
	1000	$1{\cdot}7 \times 10^4$	3700	4400	590		570	140	35	8·8	1·4	0·35	$8{\cdot}8 \times 10^{-2}$
	10^4	$1{\cdot}7 \times 10^5$	$3{\cdot}7 \times 10^4$	$4{\cdot}4 \times 10^4$	5900				350	88	14	3·5	0·88
	10^5	$1{\cdot}7 \times 10^6$	$3{\cdot}7 \times 10^5$	$4{\cdot}4 \times 10^5$	$5{\cdot}9 \times 10^4$					880	140	35	8·8
Very high	10^6	$1{\cdot}7 \times 10^7$	$3{\cdot}7 \times 10^6$	$4{\cdot}4 \times 10^6$	$5{\cdot}9 \times 10^5$							350	88

* Since water has a density of 1000 kg/m³ (approximately), the mass flow rate in kg/h of water may be obtained by multiplying this column by 1000. (Values to two significant figures.)

performance and quality of flowmeters. The main terms are discussed below.

Accuracy

It is generally accepted that accuracy refers to the truthfulness of the instrument. An instrument of high accuracy more nearly gives a true reading than an instrument of low accuracy. Accuracy, then, is a quality of the instrument. It is common to refer to a measurement as accurate or not, and we understand what is meant. However, it is unsatisfactory to refer to a measurement's accuracy of, say, 1 per cent, when, presumably, we mean that the instrument's reading will lie within a band of 99 to 101 per cent of the true reading. Thus, accuracy refers to the ability of an instrument to give a reading close to the absolute value (traceable to a National Metrology Standard).

Repeatability

The performance of a meter in a process plant, or other control loop, may not require the absolute performance level that is needed when buying and selling the liquid or gas, but may require repeatability within bounds defined by the process. A flowmeter with good repeatability is one for which the probable difference between any two successive readings, taken under constant conditions with the same observer and with only a short elapsed time, is small.

Reproducibility

This is similar to repeatability, but applies when the conditions under which the readings were taken have changed in an identifiable way such as a different observer, location, etc., or after a long time.

Uncertainty

This word is properly used to refer to the quality of the measurement, and we can correctly refer to an instrument reading having an uncertainty of 1 per cent, provided we also define under what circumstances this is valid.

Confidence level

It is not satisfactory to state an uncertainty without also indicating the probability. This is given as a confidence level and, usually, for flow measurement, this is 95 per cent. We shall assume this level in this book.

Linearity

This term is of use for instruments which give a reading approximately proportional to the true flowrate over their specified range. It then refers to the closeness within which the meter achieves a truly linear or proportional response. It is usually defined by stating the limits, for example, ± 1 per cent of flowrate, within which the response lies over a stated range. With modern signal processing this is probably less important.

Range and turndown ratio
An instrument should have a specified range, or turndown, over which its performance can be trusted. Without such a statement the values for uncertainty, linearity, etc., are inadequate. It is important to note whether the values of uncertainty, linearity, etc., are related to the actual flowrate or to the full scale flow (sometimes referred to as the URV–upper range value). For instance, 1 per cent uncertainty on rate for an instrument with a 20:1 range would be impressive, but 1 per cent of full scale for a 100:1 turndown might not be very useful at the lower end of the range.

UNCERTAINTY, U, consists of two types of error:
RANDOM ERROR (PRECISION) obtained by applying the experimental standard deviation to a set of measurements

$$S = \left\{ \frac{1}{n-1} \sum_{n=1}^{n} (x_i - \bar{x})^2 \right\}^{1/2} \tag{1.1}$$

$\bar{x}$ is mean of n measurements x_i.

PRECISION is given by $\pm tS$.
For 95 per cent confidence $t \simeq 2$.
(NOTE: REPEATABILITY IS DEFINED AS $2\sqrt{2}S$).

SYSTEMATIC ERROR (BIAS), B.

REPEATABILITY GOOD $\rightarrow$ tS small
ACCURACY GOOD $\rightarrow$ tS and B small.
REPRODUCIBILITY GOOD $\rightarrow$ tS small and effect of measurement conditions small.

Random error, sometimes called precision or experimental error, causes scatter, as the name suggests, and reflects the quality of the instrument design and construction. It may be calculated by taking a series of repeat readings resulting in the value of the experimental standard deviation. The repeatability, as defined above, is then obtained as the root sum square of the random error of two successive readings or approximately $\sqrt{2}$ times the random error.

Systematic error, according to flowmeter usage, is that which is unchanging within the period of a short test with constant conditions. However, there may be longer term drift, or change, with changes in conditions, which results in a change in the bias, and affects the reproducibility.

There is some debate about the correct way to combine the random and systematic errors. One problem is the difficulty of actually assessing the size of the systematic error. If it is assumed that in most situations where systematic errors are important, the bias will be minimized by calibration and/or adjustment, then the remaining total uncertainty will presumably consist of the root sum square of the calibration uncertainty and tS. Thus, if the experimental standard deviation is obtained from 30 or more readings, then the probability of future readings falling outside $\pm 2S$ of the mean is 1 in 20.

However, in addition, it may be necessary to allow for a change in the bias with time or changed conditions. This change or drift may be combined with the random error, conservatively, by addition

$$U = B + tS \qquad (1.2)$$

where for a 95 per cent confidence level, t, the student's value, is

for $n = 10;$ $t = 2.26$
 $n = 20;$ $t = 2.09$
 $n > 30;$ $t = 2.0$

Other confidence levels may, of course, be used.

In discussing individual flowmeter designs, where possible the likely value of uncertainty, random error (precision), or linearity will be given, with probable turndown ranges.

FLOW METER 7
SELECTION.

1.2 FLOWMETER SYSTEMS

OBJECTIVE OF FLOWMETER SYSTEM
- to deliver a signal uniquely related to the flowrate, despite the influences of installation and operating environment.

CONSIDERATIONS
- What is the operating envelope and is it defined in terms of a percentage of rate or of full scale?
- How will 'influence quantities' affect the performance?
- Is the flow steady?
- Is the effect of the fluid on the flow meter known?
- What effect will surrounding pipework have?
- Are there any special problems: vibration, pipe protection, etc?

The object of installing a flowmeter system is to obtain a measure of the flowrate, usually in the form of an electrical signal, which is unambiguous and within specified uncertainty limits. This measurement should be

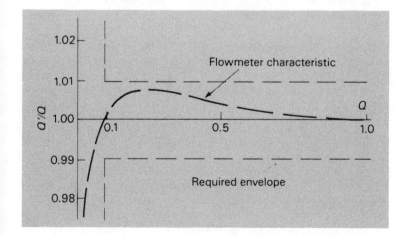

negligibly affected by the inlet and outlet pipework systems and the operating environment.

For fixed conditions in which only the flowrate is varied the ratio of measured to true flowrate should be a function of flowrate only. Ideally it will be unity (that is, linear); in practice it will lie within the sort of envelope in the above figure. This indicates a flowmeter performance for which the uncertainty is within 1 per cent of flowrate for a 10:1 turndown or range. This envelope might be a consequence of the instrument being calibrated at a point near the top of the range. The manufacturer, who probably carried out the calibration, knew from production control and sample testing that with a single adjustment the performance would lie within this envelope. It is apparent that this could equally be seen as a linearity envelope. Such performance in a flowmeter would be quite good. If, on the other hand, the uncertainty was defined in terms of full-scale flowrate or upper range value (URV), then the envelope would become trumpet shaped with an increasing uncertainty as a percentage of actual rate as the flow reduced. A 1 per cent uncertainty based on full-scale flow would give a 10 per cent uncertainty at 10 per cent of flow, based on actual flow. It is very important, therefore, that the actual operating envelope of the flowmeter is clear to the user and that it meets the user's specification. Within this operating envelope there will be a flowmeter characteristic which will be obtained by calibration over the operating range.

Flowmeter characteristic

$$\frac{Q'}{Q} = f(Q) = 1 + \delta + \frac{A_1}{(Q/Q_o)} + \frac{A_2}{(Q/Q_o)^2} \tag{1.3}$$

Where Q' is the flowmeter reading at datum conditions, Q is the actual volumetric flowrate, and Q_o is the volumetric flowrate at the calibration point (normally near or at full flow).

δ is set to a value such that $Q'/Q = 1$ when $Q/Q_o = 1$.

For a 10:1 turndown with envelope of less than 1 per cent and Q_o is URV

$$\frac{Q'}{Q} = 0.995 + \frac{0.006}{(Q/Q_o)} - \frac{0.0006}{(Q/Q_o)^2} \tag{1.4}$$

Where $\delta = -0.005$

One possible function which recognizes that flowmeters are often calibrated near the top of their range is given above. This function is given for illustration only; it should not be seen as modelling any particular flowmeter response. However, it illustrates the sort of characteristic found in some types of flowmeter. Thus, at full-scale, $Q'/Q = 1\cdot000$; at 50 per cent of full-scale $Q'/Q = 1\cdot005$; at 20 per cent, $Q'/Q = 1\cdot01$; at 10 per cent, $Q'/Q = 0\cdot995$; at 5 per cent, $Q'/Q = 0\cdot983$, an error of about -2 per cent of actual flowrate. It illustrates, although it does not prove, that one should be careful to operate the flowmeter within its prescribed accuracy envelope.

It is possible, with modern signal processing, to obtain $Q'/Q = 1$ for all values of Q/Q_o, but the danger of this is that it disguises the effect of a shift in the value of the coefficients. Any such change will have a detrimental effect on the uncertainty. However, provided this danger is kept under review by regular recalibration, it is useful to be able to store in the flow computer the characteristic for the operating range. The computer will then calculate from the flowmeter's signals, the actual flowrate to within the uncertainty defined by the meter's repeatability and the calibration stand uncertainty.

CHANGES FROM DATUM

$$\frac{Q''}{Q'} = (1 + C_T\Delta T)(1 + C_D\Delta D)(\quad)\ldots$$

$$= \Pi(1 + C_T\Delta T) \tag{1.5}$$

Where Q'' is the flowmeter reading affected by changes from datum, Π indicates 'the product of', C_T, etc., are essentially the sensitivity coefficients, and ΔT, etc. are the parametric changes in the influence quantities.

An essential feature of a high quality instrument is that these changes are small and consequently

$$\Pi(1 + C_T\Delta T) \approx 1 + \Sigma C_T\Delta T \tag{1.6}$$

Combining (1.3), (1.5), and (1.6) we obtain

$$\frac{Q''}{Q} = 1 + \delta + \frac{A}{(Q/Q_o)} + \frac{B}{(Q/Q_o)^2} + \Sigma C_T\Delta T \tag{1.7}$$

The dimensional sensitivity coefficient will differ according to the flowmeter type. The changes in fluid and environment will affect the flowmeter reading. Temperature change ΔT will cause expansion of the materials of the flowmeter resulting in area change, changes in clearances, and changes in important dimensions, as well as changes in fluid viscosity, and so on. Some of these effects, or influence quantities, may be compensated for with temperature sensing, etc., if the sensitivity coefficients are known, but this is unlikely to deal with all the changes. It is necessary when calibrating a flowmeter system to set all parameters to agreed datum values.

As an example of the size of the temperature expansion, for steel with an expansion per °C of 11×10^{-6} and for a $\Delta T = 10°C$ then length change is 0·01 per cent and area change is 0·02 per cent. To calculate the error from these effects it is necessary to obtain $\sqrt{\{\Sigma(C_T \Delta T)^2\}}$.

The unsteadiness of the fluid may affect both the transducer and the signal measurement system. This may be caused by both sources upstream and downstream of the flowmeter system. The fluid itself may be well documented but may never have been used with certain types of flowmeter. The flow may be occasionally multiphase and the meter may be expected to respond to such flows.

The pipework, upstream particularly, but downstream also, has an effect on virtually all flowmeters and must be considered in identifying a flowmeter site and in selecting an instrument. There are also such problems downstream as pipework which allows a flowmeter to run partially empty.

Sources of vibration, electrolytic pipe protection, pipework stresses, pipework material, etc., will all need to be considered in selecting a flowmeter system.

In this section an attempt has been made to indicate the nature of the problem. It is very complex and it will not be easy to account for every effect. It is, however, important to define a datum with care to include:

temperature datum;
pressure datum;
fluid characteristics;
datum flow profile;
steady conditions.

Dominant among these is the flow behaviour, and it is useful to have some understanding of it both to understand its effect on uncertainty, and also more generally to understand the behaviour of the instruments.

1.3   FLOW IN PIPES

1.3.1   Flow similarity

FLOW SIMILARITY
Reynolds experiment.
Laminar and turbulent flow profiles.
Reynolds Number $= \dfrac{\rho VD}{\mu} = \dfrac{\text{Inertia forces}}{\text{Viscous forces}}$.

One of the most important concepts in fluid mechanics is similarity of flows. Much of what we shall discuss in this book is concerned with the concept that flows in two different pipes are similar in various ways providing certain relationships are satisfied.

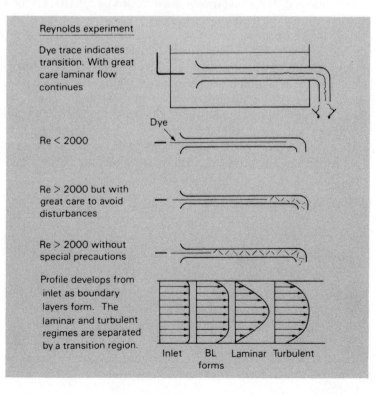

Reynolds experiment

Dye trace indicates transition. With great care laminar flow continues

Dye

Re < 2000

Re > 2000 but with great care to avoid disturbances

Re > 2000 without special precautions

Profile develops from inlet as boundary layers form. The laminar and turbulent regimes are separated by a transition region.

Inlet   BL   Laminar Turbulent
         forms

Osborne Reynolds (1883) set up an experiment as shown above. In this experiment a dye streak is produced along the axis of a pipe through which water flows. The flow into the pipe is smooth, and for low flowrates the dye streak experiences very little change. However, although this behaviour can be sustained to high flowrates it is found that there is a critical condition below which the streak will always be well defined, but above which any disturbance in the flow will be magnified and the dye streak will be broken up by eddies. The condition is given by the Reynolds number (Re) which provides an indication of the ratio of inertia forces in the flow to viscous forces

$$\text{Re} = \frac{\rho V D}{\mu} \tag{1.8}$$

where ρ is the fluid density, μ the viscosity, V the velocity, and D the pipe diameter in consistent units. For Re less than about 2000 the flow in the tube is laminar and all the fluid travels in a direction parallel to the pipe axis (neglecting Brownian motion which leads to a slight blurring of the streakliness). Above this value of Re disturbances will probably grow, forming turbulent eddies, so that, superimposed on the axial flow, there are circulating eddies of many sizes with velocities up to about one-tenth of the axial velocity for a smooth pipe. The effect of these turbulent eddies is to mix up the flow and to create a more uniform profile in the pipe.

The importance of flow similarity is that, for two geometrically similar pipes, the flow behaviour will be the same for equal values of Re in each pipe. If we specify, therefore, for calibration of a flowmeter, a certain value of Re and a certain pipe geometry, then we know that this flow will be well defined.

1.3.2 Pipe flow losses and profiles

LAMINAR FLOW
   Velocity $\propto$ pressure drop.
   Profile parabolic.

TURBULENT FLOW
   Velocity $\propto \sqrt{(\text{Pressure drop})}$.
   Profile flattened by turbulent mixing.

We may obtain the losses in laminar flow since the shear stress between layers of fluid at position y from the wall is given by

$$\tau = \mu \frac{\mathrm{d}V}{\mathrm{d}y} \tag{1.9}$$

and the gradient of velocity at the wall will give the shear stress. In this equation μ is the dynamic (or absolute) viscosity.

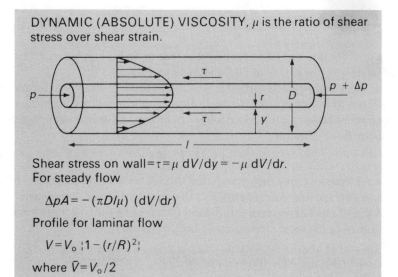

DYNAMIC (ABSOLUTE) VISCOSITY, μ is the ratio of shear stress over shear strain.

Shear stress on wall $= \tau = \mu \, \mathrm{d}V/\mathrm{d}y = -\mu \, \mathrm{d}V/\mathrm{d}r$.
For steady flow

$\Delta pA = -(\pi D/\mu) \, (\mathrm{d}V/\mathrm{d}r)$

Profile for laminar flow

$V = V_0 \{1 - (r/R)^2\}$

where $\bar{V} = V_0/2$

We may balance the forces on the inner tube of fluid

$$\pi r^2 \Delta p = 2\pi r l \tau \tag{1.10}$$

$$\frac{\mathrm{d}V}{\mathrm{d}r} = -\frac{r\Delta p}{2\mu l} \tag{1.11}$$

$$V = \frac{\Delta p}{2\mu l} \int_r^R r \, \mathrm{d}r = \frac{1}{4} \frac{\Delta p}{\mu l} (R^2 - r^2) \tag{1.12}$$

where V is zero at the wall of the pipe due to the non-slip condition for a fluid at a solid boundary. This gives a parabolic profile for V across the pipe. If we obtain the mean velocity in the pipe from this we shall be able to relate the pressure loss to the mean velocity.

$$\bar{V} = \frac{1}{4} \frac{\Delta p}{\mu l} \frac{1}{\pi R^2} \int_0^R 2\pi \, r \, (R^2 - r^2) \, \mathrm{d}r$$

$$= \frac{1}{8} \frac{\Delta p}{\mu l} R^2 \tag{1.13}$$

$$\Delta p = 8 \frac{\mu l \bar{V}}{R^2} \tag{1.14}$$

It is important to note the linear dependence of Δp on $\bar{V}$ in laminar flow as we shall find this is rare in fluid mechanical losses.

As soon as the flow is turbulent we need to resort to empirical formulae for losses and flow profiles in which Δp is proportional to $\bar{V}^2$. In order to systematise losses we introduce a loss coefficient, K, sometimes called the velocity head constant.

$$\Delta p = \tfrac{1}{2} \rho \, \bar{V}^2 \, K \tag{1.15}$$

The pressure loss may then be referred to as K velocity heads, and we find this has an approximately constant value for a particular component.

A useful set of approximate turbulent flow profiles (not the most precise, but possibly the most convenient to use) are given below.

APPROXIMATE EXPRESSION FOR TURBULENT PROFILES

$$V = V_\mathrm{o} \left(1 - \frac{r}{R} \right)^{1/n} \tag{1.16}$$

where V_o is the velocity on the axis and

$$\bar{V} = \frac{2 \, n^2 V_\mathrm{o}}{(1 + 2n)(1 + n)}$$

The table below then gives the value of n related to a particular value of Re

Re	$2 \cdot 3 \times 10^4$	$1 \cdot 1 \times 10^5$	$1 \cdot 1 \times 10^6$	2×10^6	$3 \cdot 2 \times 10^6$
n	6·6	7·0	8·8	10	10
$V(0 \cdot 75R)/\bar{V}$	1·0041	1·0045	1·0054	1·0055	1·0055

The last line of the table is interesting as it suggests that if one cannot afford a flowmeter but needs to obtain the mean pipe velocity as precisely as possible using one local velocity measurement, then one should place a local velocity probe at a three-quarter radius position. Laminar and turbulent profile shapes are illustrated below.

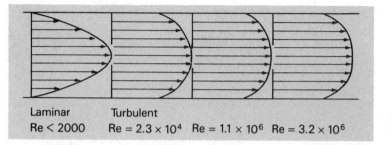

Laminar
Re < 2000

Turbulent
Re = 2.3×10^4 Re = 1.1×10^6 Re = 3.2×10^6

These profiles all assume that there is a sufficient length of straight pipe to ensure that they are fully developed. For turbulent flow this is usually taken as about 60 diameters ($60D$).

Some fluids metered may display "Non-Newtonian" behaviour by which is meant that μ is not constant for a given temperature and pressure, but is a function of the shearing conditions in the fluid and/or the rate of change of shear with time. This may influence the flowmeter performance by its effect on flow profile shape within a pipe, and also by its effect on the local flow patterns around the internal geometry of the flowmeter. It is unlikely that any data will be available on the effects of a Non-Newtonian fluid on a particular flowmeter.

1.3.3 Boundary layers

It might be possible to write this book without referring to a boundary layer, but the concept is so important that it is better to deal with the subject briefly.

There seemed to be an unbridgeable gap between experimental hydraulics and theoretical hydrodynamics until Prandtl produced his theory (1904) of the boundary layer. One example of the gap was the observed ability of a body to produce lift and the inability of the theory to predict this (diagram (a) below). Boundary layer theory was able to reconcile these conflicting positions. The boundary layer is unable to negotiate a sudden change in flow direction and leaves the trailing edge tangentially so that there can be no pressure change across the trailing edge.

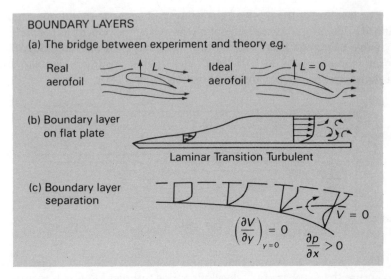

BOUNDARY LAYERS

(a) The bridge between experiment and theory e.g.

Real aerofoil   Ideal aerofoil $L = 0$

(b) Boundary layer on flat plate

Laminar Transition Turbulent

(c) Boundary layer separation

$V = 0$

$$\left(\frac{\partial V}{\partial y}\right)_{y=0} = 0 \qquad \frac{\partial p}{\partial x} > 0$$

It is also useful to consider the growth of a boundary layer on a flat plate. The diagram (b) above greatly exaggerates the thickness of the boundary layer by showing an outer edge to it. Initially the boundary layer is laminar. Flow is all essentially in the direction parallel to the plate. After a certain upstream length the flow becomes unstable so that small disturbances grow and an intermittent eddying motion results creating a transition region. Progressing further downstream the disturbances have now occurred throughout the layer creating a fully turbulent boundary layer. The diagram (b) also indicates the change in shape of the boundary layer from laminar with a nearly linear wall region, to turbulent with a rapid rise in velocity near the wall and a more uniform velocity across the layer resulting from the turbulent mixing. Typical values of boundary layer thickness, lest the diagram mislead the reader, are that after 2·5 m of flat plate for a Reynolds number of 10^7 (based on the plate length), the thickness could be about 5 mm if laminar and about 40 mm if turbulent (at $Re = 10^7$ it is just conceivable that, with care, a laminar boundary layer could exist, although a turbulent transition would normally have occurred).

In an adverse gradient the boundary layer thickens as shown in (c) above, until a condition is reached where the gradient of velocity at the surface $(\partial V/\partial y) = 0$ and separation occurs with reverse flow near the surface. Such a flow is caused by an adverse pressure gradient such as that occurring in a diffusing flow. It leads to energy loss in the flow.

1.3.4 Equations for pressure change

> PRESSURE CHANGE WITH AREA
> Continuity equation
> *plus*
> Bernoulli's equation
> *gives*
> Pressure change equation

The application of a certain type of flowmeter may be strongly influenced by the pressure loss which its installation would create. It is, therefore, important to have some understanding of pressure loss. In equation 1.15 we introduced a loss coefficient. Below we derive the relationship between pressure change and velocity change

The first equation which we need to consider is the continuity equation. This is a simple statement of the assumption that the fluid is a continuum and that the same mass flow must cross each section of the pipe.

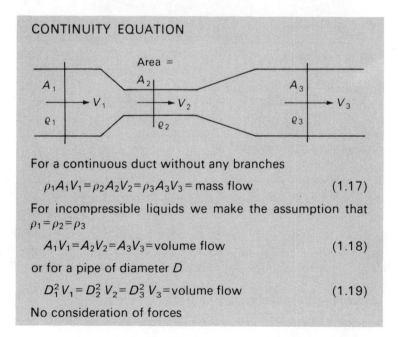

CONTINUITY EQUATION

For a continuous duct without any branches

$$\rho_1 A_1 V_1 = \rho_2 A_2 V_2 = \rho_3 A_3 V_3 = \text{mass flow} \qquad (1.17)$$

For incompressible liquids we make the assumption that $\rho_1 = \rho_2 = \rho_3$

$$A_1 V_1 = A_2 V_2 = A_3 V_3 = \text{volume flow} \qquad (1.18)$$

or for a pipe of diameter D

$$D_1^2 V_1 = D_2^2 V_2 = D_3^2 V_3 = \text{volume flow} \qquad (1.19)$$

No consideration of forces

If the assumption can be made that the fluid is incompressible – an adequate assumption for many situations with liquids flowing – then the density will be constant through the duct and the equation reduces to one of constant volume flow. This may also be written in terms of diameter, D, for a pipe flow (equation 1.19).

In particular

$$V_2 = V_1 \, D_1^2/D_2^2 \tag{1.20}$$

This equation of continuity is concerned with the effect of duct geometry on the motion. No consideration is given to forces acting on the flow. In particular we have assumed that the flow is one-dimensional so that one value of velocity is sufficient to specify the velocity at a cross section. However, we have seen above that this is not so.

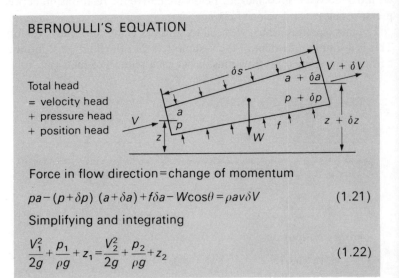

BERNOULLI'S EQUATION

Total head
= velocity head
+ pressure head
+ position head

Force in flow direction = change of momentum

$$pa - (p + \delta p)\,(a + \delta a) + f\delta a - W\cos\theta = \rho a v \delta V \tag{1.21}$$

Simplifying and integrating

$$\frac{V_1^2}{2g} + \frac{p_1}{\rho g} + z_1 = \frac{V_2^2}{2g} + \frac{p_2}{\rho g} + z_2 \tag{1.22}$$

The second equation which we require relates velocity, pressure, and head or height above some datum. It relates the forces acting on the fluid to the change in momentum through a control volume. It is known as Bernoulli's equation.

Bernoulli's equation may be expressed in the form:

velocity head + pressure head + position head = total head

where the total head is constant along any streamline in the absence of losses. The word 'head' is used because the units in which the equation is often written are those of length, height being the appropriate length-dimension in this case.

The numerical expression is obtained by taking the balance of forces on the duct flow

Force in direction of flow =
inlet pressure force −
outlet pressure + force on longitudinal surface −
component of weight =

$$pa - (p + \delta p)(a + \delta a) + f\delta a - W\cos\theta$$

where $p \leqslant f \leqslant p + \delta p$ (or value between the extremes) and we write this as $f = p + \delta p'$

Also

$$W = \rho\left(a + \frac{\delta a}{2}\right)\delta sg$$

So that the force in the direction of flow

$$= -p\delta a - a\delta p - \delta a\delta p + p\delta a + \delta a\delta p' - \rho\left(a + \frac{\delta a}{2}\right)\delta sg \cos\theta$$

This must create a rate of change of momentum

$$= \rho(a + \delta a)(V + \delta V)^2 - \rho aV^2$$

$$= \rho aV\{(V + \delta V) - V\}$$

$$= \rho aV\delta V$$

So

$$\rho aV\delta V = -a\delta p - \rho ag\delta s \cos\theta$$

and on integrating between two points in ducts 1 and 2 (with constant density) we obtain equation (1.22).

We note from this equation that, as velocity increases, pressure decreases for constant z. In most pipe flowmeters the change in z should be negligible or compensated for by the liquid level in tubes connecting the pressure tapping to the pressure gauge.

We may now combine equations (1.20) and (1.22) so that, in a duct of variable area, we may relate the velocity in the pipe to the pressure reduction from 1 to 2.

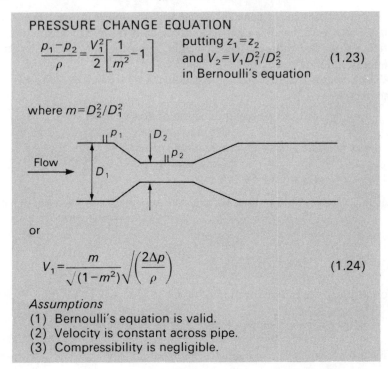

PRESSURE CHANGE EQUATION

$$\frac{p_1 - p_2}{\rho} = \frac{V_1^2}{2}\left[\frac{1}{m^2} - 1\right]$$

putting $z_1 = z_2$
and $V_2 = V_1 D_1^2 / D_2^2$
in Bernoulli's equation

(1.23)

where $m = D_2^2 / D_1^2$

or

$$V_1 = \frac{m}{\sqrt{(1 - m^2)}}\sqrt{\left(\frac{2\Delta p}{\rho}\right)}$$

(1.24)

Assumptions
(1) Bernoulli's equation is valid.
(2) Velocity is constant across pipe.
(3) Compressibility is negligible.

The assumptions above are amplified below:

(1) Bernoulli's equation is only strictly valid along a streamline where no change in total head occurs. We have neglected losses due to viscosity.
(2) The velocity is constant across the pipe section. This is clearly an incorrect assumption since the velocity always varies across a pipe and the shape of the profile will vary through the duct as it varies in size.
(3) Compressibility is negligible. For gases even small changes in density between 1 and 2 may affect the validity of the equation, if it is to be used for flow measurement of high precision.

In addition, we shall see later on that in some applications we will not precisely know the value of D_2 because of flow 'separation' and also in many cases losses will require that we introduce the loss coefficient (defined by equation (1.15)) as a method of using equation (1.22) where it is not strictly applicable.

1.4 FLOWS DUE TO BENDS AND AREA CHANGE

Pipe fittings, such as bends, valves, area changes:
- disturb the profile for flowmeters and cause installation errors;
- create pressure losses.

So far we have considered the flow in a straight pipe. In most flowmeter installations it will be very difficult to achieve an adequate length of straight pipe upstream of the flowmeter to ensure that the flow profile is fully developed. More often the flow profile will be distorted by a bend upstream or an area change due to a contraction, expansion, or a valve in the pipework. This profile distortion will affect the flow for several diameters downstream and such fittings will also lead to additional flow losses.

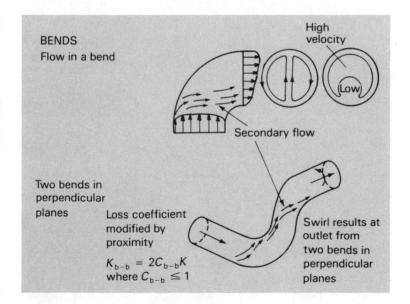

BENDS
Flow in a bend

High velocity

(Low)

Secondary flow

Two bends in perpendicular planes

Loss coefficient modified by proximity

$$K_{b-b} = 2C_{b-b}K$$
where $C_{b-b} \leq 1$

Swirl results at outlet from two bends in perpendicular planes

1.4.1 Bends

The flow in a bend has been quite extensively documented, due both to its importance industrially and also, presumably to its being partially tractable theoretically. It is often very difficult to separate flowmeters from bends adequately to ensure that the distorted profile from the bend has disappeared. The profile will affect the behaviour of a flowmeter calibrated on a fully developed turbulent profile.

The diagrams above indicate the flow in the bend and show approximate contours of the velocity after the bend. For $\theta = 90$ degrees and an $r/D = 2$, the value of K, the loss coefficient, is given as $0{\cdot}16$ for an $Re = 10^6$. Corrections are then available for other values of Re, pipe roughness, outlet tangent length, and so on.

Two bends in succession at right angles cause swirl which is a very dominant flow feature and takes tens of diameters to decay. The diagram indicates the causes of the swirl. Swirl may also be caused by combinations of valves and bends and by pipe junctions. Because of its slow decay it is particularly important to remove it using flow straighteners (discussed below) to prevent it affecting flowmeters downstream.

The loss due to two bends in close proximity for ranges of spacing, L, of

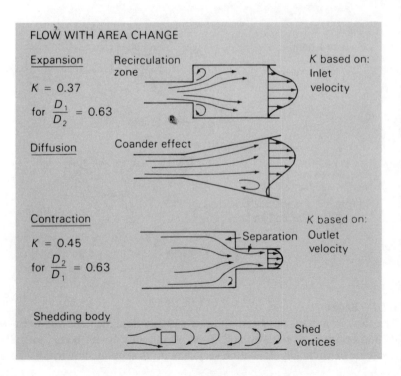

FLOW WITH AREA CHANGE

Expansion Recirculation zone K based on: Inlet velocity

$K = 0.37$

for $\dfrac{D_1}{D_2} = 0.63$

Diffusion Coander effect

Contraction K based on: Outlet velocity

$K = 0.45$

for $\dfrac{D_2}{D_1} = 0.63$

Separation

Shedding body Shed vortices

4–30 diameters is little affected by the relative orientation of the bends. The total loss is given by (Miller, 1978)

$$K_{b-b} = 2\, C_{b-b} K$$

where a typical value of C_{b-b} for $r/D = 2$ and $L/D = 4$ is 0·7.

1.4.2 Changes in area

Flow through an expansion leads to a submerged jet flow. The flow as it issues from the smaller inlet pipe sheds vorticity which creates the recirculation zone. The profile in the larger outlet pipe will be peaked due to the jet.

The flow out of the diffuser will face an increasing pressure and the boundary layer will thicken on the walls again leading to a peaked profile. At a diffuser half-angle greater than about 7 degrees the flow becomes detached from one wall and flows along the other wall. This is known as the coander effect and is used in the fluidic flowmeter.

The flow in a contraction, although experiencing a decreasing pressure gradient may create separation bubbles of reverse flow just inside the smaller tube. These are followed by reattachment and the flow generally results in a flattening of the profile. At first sight it seems surprising that K is greater for the contraction than for the expansion. If we relate this to pressure loss we find (Miller, 1978)

(Expansion) $\quad \Delta P_E = \frac{1}{2}\rho V_{E_1}^2 \times 0\cdot37$

(Contraction) $\quad \Delta P_C = \frac{1}{2}\rho V_{C_2}^2 \times 0\cdot45$

If

$$V_{C_2} = V_{E_1}$$

then

$$\frac{\Delta p_E}{\Delta p_C} = \frac{0\cdot37}{0\cdot45} = 0\cdot82$$

However, the pressure loss for the contraction is reduced if the inlet edge is rounded, and $\Delta p_E / \Delta p_C > 1$ if the area ratio is less than 0·3.

The bluff body in the duct causes vortices to be shed due to the vorticity which comes from the sharp detachment points. The frequency of shedding can be thought of as related to the time taken for the shed vorticity to fill a large vortex.

1.5   FLOW STRAIGHTENERS AND CONDITIONERS

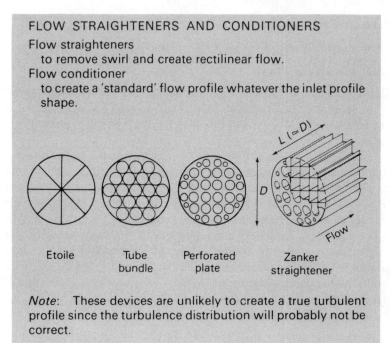

FLOW STRAIGHTENERS AND CONDITIONERS

Flow straighteners
    to remove swirl and create rectilinear flow.
Flow conditioner
    to create a 'standard' flow profile whatever the inlet profile shape.

Etoile   Tube bundle   Perforated plate   Zanker straightener

Note: These devices are unlikely to create a true turbulent profile since the turbulence distribution will probably not be correct.

Because of the profile distortion resulting from upstream fittings, attempts have been made to produce a pipe fitting which will return the flow from its distorted form to the fully developed datum.

The distinction between flow straighteners and flow conditioners is introduced to reinforce the point that the straightener only removes swirl. This may be adequate as swirl is found, otherwise, to be extremely persistent. Two common forms of straightener are the Etoile constructed from a star of flat plates, and the tube bundle. It is important in both to ensure that they are constructed with care as they can introduce swirl as well as remove it. The perforated plate is similar to the time honoured method from aerodynamics experiments of graded gauzes and is used to create a flow profile approximating to a turbulent profile. It does not result in the removal of swirl.

The Zanker design combines both features in an attempt to create a profile without swirl which is of the correct shape required by the flowmeter calibration datum.

However, although more work has been done recently on flow conditioners it is very unlikely that any designs achieve a profile which is a true fully developed turbulent profile, since they are unlikely to achieve the correct turbulence distribution, and this is likely to introduce small changes in a flowmeter's performance.

1.6 FLUID PARAMETERS

We need to review briefly the main parameters used in flow measurement and list their units and typical values. Although the main concern of this book is with flow measurement a very brief review of other measurements is necessary.

1.6.1 Pressure

PRESSURE

Pressure, p = force per unit area
    (SI unit N/m^2 or Pascal)
    Also in common use bar: 1 bar = 10^5 N/m^2 (this is approximately one atmosphere).

Pressure head is a commonly used quantity

    e.g., Bernoulli $\dfrac{V^2}{2g}+\dfrac{p}{\rho g}+z$ = total head = H

Pressure = $\rho A h g /A$
     = $\rho g h$

Head = $\dfrac{p}{\rho g}$

The SI unit of pressure is Newtons/metre^2 (N/m^2) or Pascal (Pa), but the bar is commonly used as it is a more convenient size.

Pressure acts equally in all directions. It is useful on occasion to refer to pressure as a 'head'. The relationship between head and pressure is easily derived for a certain depth of liquid.

Bernoulli's equation may be expressed in heads, and from the diagram in the box above the (ideal) changing balance between the three heads can be seen. Thus, in the tank, at its surface, p is zero, taking it as the value above atmospheric pressure (gauge pressure, g, as opposed to absolute pressure,

a; e.g., psia for pounds per square inch absolute, bar a for bar absolute), V is zero, and $z = H$. At section 1, z is small and the velocity is large due to the small pipe area. The balance will give p, which will be less than at a point inside the tank at the same level. At section 2, z is large, the velocity is less due to the greater cross-section, and p will make up the difference. At 3, the pressure is atmospheric, so $p = 0$, z is small, and most of the head will be velocity or kinetic head. Ideally the fountain would just rise to the level of H.

Some useful pressure comparisons are shown below.

> **ONE ATMOSPHERE**
> $= 101\,325$ N/m^2
> $= 101\,325$ Pa
> $= 101 \cdot 325$ kPa
> $= 1 \cdot 01325$ bar
> $= 760$ mm Mercury (Hg)
> $= 10 \cdot 3$ m Water (H$_2$O)
> $= 820$ mm of water-over-mercury in a manometer
> $= 14 \cdot 71$ psi (lb/in^2).
>
> Note also for gas volume correction
> Metric Standard Reference Conditions: 15°C and 1013·25 mbar Dry
> Normal Temperature and Pressure: 0°C and 1013·25 mbar (SI equivalent values).

The measurement of pressure is an essential part of many flowmetering installations. The measurement of the pressure in the pipe requires that we make a hole in the pipe wall and measure the pressure at that hole. This will give us the value of p in the diagram below, which is known as the 'static pressure'.

Errors can arise from pressure tappings which must be made clean and sharp (not chamfered) and without burrs. In order to obtain a mean pressure a piezometer ring may be used. The preferred type is the triple 'T' shown in the box below. The connecting tubes must be carefully laid to avoid, in the case of a liquid, gas pockets or, in the case of a gas, condensation pockets. Either of these may affect the pressure reading. Adequate bleed points should be provided and, if possible, transparent tubing should be used.

Pressure measurement is usually by one of three main methods.

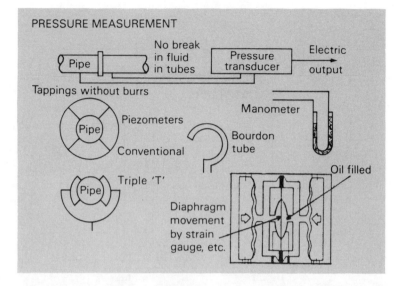

PRESSURE MEASUREMENT

Pipe — No break in fluid in tubes — Pressure transducer — Electric output

Tappings without burrs

Pipe — Piezometers

Pipe — Conventional

Pipe — Triple 'T'

Manometer

Bourdon tube

Oil filled

Diaphragm movement by strain gauge, etc.

A manometer which balances the pressure to be measured against a height of liquid. Hence the reason for giving values of pressure above in terms of mm mercury, etc. They are subject to errors, such as tube contamination, and depend on the precision of the tube bore and of the meniscus reading. A liquid giving an adequate displacement may not be compatible with a wide range of readings. Manometers with an electrical signal output are available, but expensive.

A Bourdon Gauge which has a flattened tube wound into an arc. The tube unwinds under pressure since its flat cross section becomes more oval and the increased distance between the arcs of inner and outer radii is accommodated by unwinding. A differential pressure version requires the outside of the tube to be pressurized.

A transducer which consists of a diaphragm which deflects under a differential pressure. The deflection, which is very small, may be measured by a strain gauge, capacitance change, vibrating element, or other method.

Referring to equation (1.22) it can be seen that if the flow is brought to rest along a horizontal streamline, then a pressure p_o will result.

This is known as the 'total pressure' (or $p_o/\rho g$ as the 'total head'). It may be achieved by using a pitot tube, a tube with its axis aligned with the flow and its open end, where the flow is brought to rest, towards the flow. If the

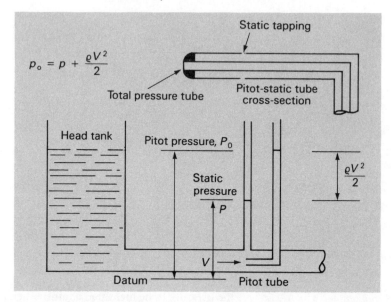

$$p_o = p + \frac{\varrho V^2}{2}$$

Total pressure tube

Static tapping

Pitot-static tube cross-section

Head tank

Pitot pressure, P_0

Static pressure

P

$\frac{\varrho V^2}{2}$

V

Datum

Pitot tube

difference between total and static pressures is measured with a differential pressure device then, knowing ρ, the density, v, can be obtained.

1.6.2 Temperature

The SI unit of temperature, T, is the degree Celsius (°C) or on an absolute scale the Kelvin (K). It is compared below with the Fahrenheit scale (°F).

It is important to remember that when we speak of errors in temperature measurement we need either to give an error in °C or an error as a

	°C	K	°F
Absolute zero	−273·15	0	−459·67
Ice point	0	273·15	32
Ambient range	10	283·15	50
	20	293·15	68
	30	303·15	86
	40	313·15	104
Boiling point	100	373·15	212

Types of thermometer	Approximate range °C
Mercury in glass	−40 to +650
Other liquids	−80 to +300
Platinum resistance	−200 to +650
Thermistor	−40 to +300
Thermocouples	−200 to 1700
Gas thermometer	−270 to 650

percentage of temperature difference. The common methods of temperature measurement are listed in the box below.

The choice will be influenced by whether or not an electrical output signal is required, the range, the accuracy required, convenience, and price. The platinum resistance (PRT), thermistor, and thermocouple provide a direct electrical output. It should be remembered that the thermocouple is essentially a temperature difference device and it may not always be convenient to retain one of the thermocouple junctions at, say, melting ice temperature. This is avoided in some commercial instruments by measuring the cold junction temperature with a different sensor and correcting the reading.

The PRT with resistance set to 100 Ω for 0°C is an important industrial instrument.

1.6.3 Density

The SI unit of density, ρ, is kilograms/metre³ (kg/m³). The density of water at 0°C is approximately:

$$1000 \text{ Kg/m}^3 \quad = 1 \text{ gm/cm}^3 \quad \approx 62 \cdot 4 \text{ lb/ft}^3.$$

Specific volume is the reciprocal of density. Specific gravity is seldom used today, but it is defined as the ratio of the density of a material to the density of water at 60°F. It has been replaced by Relative Density (T_1/T_2°C or °F)

$$= \frac{\text{Liquid density at } T_1 \text{°C(°F)}}{\text{Density of water at } T_2 \text{°C(°F)}}$$

The thermal expansion coefficient, β (sometimes α), also known as the coefficient of volumetric or cubical expansion, is the fractional increase in specific volume, v, or decrease in density, ρ, due to an increase in temperature of $1°C$.

$$\beta = -\frac{1}{\rho}\frac{d\rho}{dT} = \frac{1}{v}\frac{dv}{dT}$$

Water is an anomalous substance in that β is negative between $0°C$ and $4°C$. Compressibility for a liquid, k, is the fractional decrease in specific volume or increase in density due to a change in pressure of 1 N/m^2.

$$k = \frac{1}{\rho}\frac{d\rho}{dp} = -\frac{1}{v}\frac{dv}{dp}$$

It should be remembered that for an ideal gas

$$\frac{p}{\rho} = pv = RT$$

So for an ideal gas

$$\beta = \frac{1}{v}\frac{dv}{dT} = \frac{R}{pv} \quad \text{at constant pressure}$$

The density of a liquid can be calculated from a knowledge of the mass of a known volume of the liquid. A gas density may also be obtained in this way, but the sensitivity of the mass balance needed to obtain a precise value will be very high.

Several commercial instruments are available which make use of a change in natural frequency of vibration, either of an element immersed in the liquid or gas, or of a pipe through which the liquid or gas flows.

Below are some typical values of density, specific gravity (s.g.), and β.

	ρ	s.g.	β
Mercury	13600	136	
Water	1000	1·0	0·0002
Hydrocarbon-like	700–900	0·7–0·9	0·001
Air	1·2	0·0012	0·0034

1.6.4 Viscosity

VISCOSITY

Dynamic (Absolute) viscosity, μ, is the ratio of shear stress over shear strain.
The SI unit is the Pascal second (Pas); in more common use is the centipoise (cP)
$$1 \text{ cP} = 10^{-3} \text{ Pas.}$$

Kinematic viscosity, $v = \mu/\rho$
SI unit: m^2/s; in more common use is the centistoke (cSt)
$$1 \text{ cSt} = 10^{-6} \text{ m}^2/s = 1 \text{ mm}^2/s$$

Approximate values for 20°C and 1 bar	water	air
μ cP	1·0	0·018
v cSt	1·0	15

Liquid viscosity decreases with temperature while gas viscosity increases with temperature except at very high pressures.

There are two main methods of measuring the viscosity of a liquid or gas. The first uses the pressure loss in an orifice or a length of capillary under laminar flow conditions to obtain μ from equation (1.14). The second method obtains the torque exerted by a thin layer of the liquid or gas between two cylinders, one rotating and the other stationary. Other methods make use of a sphere falling or a bubble rising through the liquid.

There are a variety of special measures of viscosity such as Saybolt seconds and Redwood. Information on these as well as a valuable range of viscosity data will be found in Miller (1983) for many industrially metered fluids.

1.7 MULTIPHASE FLOWS

The term multiphase flow is somewhat misleading as it covers both multicomponent and multiphase. Thus dirty gas flows, air in water, cavitation, and steam may all, within this wide terminology, be termed two-phase flows. Because of the dearth of data, the flowmeter engineer will attempt to learn from data from different sources. Below we give three examples of such flows to indicate the complexity. The first example is from the flow in an oil well.

1.7.1 Vertical multiphase flows

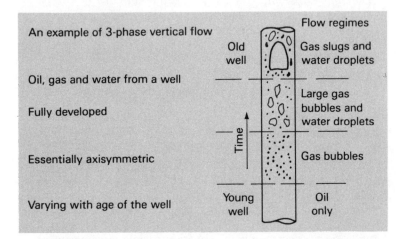

An example of 3-phase vertical flow

Oil, gas and water from a well

Fully developed

Essentially axisymmetric

Varying with age of the well

Old well

Young well

Time

Flow regimes

Gas slugs and water droplets

Large gas bubbles and water droplets

Gas bubbles

Oil only

We may consider first of all the flow in an oil well, making the assumption that this is vertical. This is not strictly true, but will give us some basic concepts. When the flow reaches the well head it will have traversed a distance equivalent to as much as 30 000 pipe diameters. The flow will therefore, presumably, be fully developed. Initially the flow will be single phase, essentially oil only. As the well pressure falls, gas bubbles will appear due to saturation of the oil. This is known as bubbly flow. With further ageing the gas bubbles will become larger. An equilibrium size distribution will result from break up due to turbulence, and coalescence due to the breakdown of the liquid film on close approach of two bubbles. However, water droplets are also now likely to be present, forming a third phase. Yet further ageing will result in the gas forming large slugs which travel up the centre of the pipe leaving a slower moving wall layer of liquid (which may even reverse during the bubble passage). These slugs may be up to 20 m long and may form an equilibrium size distribution giving a balance between coalescence due to bubbles overtaking each other, and break up due to instabilities when they become too large. Surrounding these bubbles will be smaller bubbles and droplets.

1.7.2 Horizontal two-phase flow

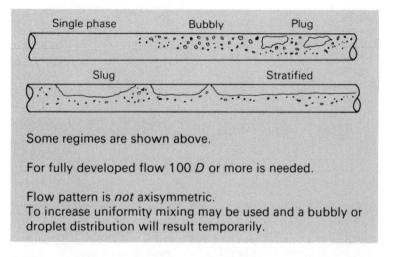

Single phase   Bubbly   Plug

Slug   Stratified

Some regimes are shown above.

For fully developed flow 100 *D* or more is needed.

Flow pattern is *not* axisymmetric.
To increase uniformity mixing may be used and a bubbly or droplet distribution will result temporarily.

We next consider horizontal two-phase flows. The most obvious change is the loss of axisymmetry. Gravity now causes the less dense phase to migrate to the top of the pipe. Thus, in a gas liquid flow the gas will move to the top of the pipe as bubbles. If these are allowed to become large, plugs of gas result, and as these coalesce slugs of gas take up regions against the top of the pipe. Eventually a sufficient number of these will lead to a stratified flow.

Alternatively, the mixtures may be of two liquids such as water in oil. The droplets of water will sink towards the bottom of the pipe, mirroring the behaviour of air bubbles, and will eventually drop out onto the bottom of the pipe causing a continuous layer of water.

With sufficient straight pipe (100 *D* or more) a fully developed flow may be achieved. However, although flow pattern maps have been made to predict the nature of the flow in a pipe, the many parameters affecting the flow and the unlikelihood of adequate pipe length to give fully developed flow make it likely that in most applications we shall not be able to predict the resulting flow or how it will effect a flowmeter. It may be possible to mix the fluid to distribute the second phase, but this will cause severe turbulence and a changing profile, conditions generally considered unsuitable for flowmeter installation.

1.7.3   Steam

STEAM

Superheated
   – treat as a gas
wet steam
   – e.g., 95% by mass vapour   ⎫
          5% by mass liquid   ⎬   difficult to meter
Limiting assumptions
   – droplets do not affect flowmeter so response is proportional to vapour flow
   – flowmeter measures total mass or volume flow

Another (and truly) two-phase fluid is steam. Superheated steam may be treated as a gas and its properties are well tabulated. However, it is of increasing importance to measure the flow of wet steam. This is steam made up of, say, about 95 per cent (by mass) of vapour and about 5 per cent of liquid. The droplets of liquid are carried by the vapour, but will not follow the vapour stream precisely. As with water droplets in oil, the liquid will drop through the vapour to land on the pipe wall and we may obtain an annular flow regime until sufficient turbulence is created to re-entrain this liquid. The measurement of such a flow poses major problems since the pressure and temperature remain constant while the dryness varies. We are, therefore, unable to deduce dryness or density from the pressure and temperature, and apart from flowmeter errors caused by the wet steam, we shall not be able to obtain the mass flow from which the heat content is deduced. Two limiting assumptions are suggested above, but neither may be adequate. In one case it might be assumed that the small droplets of liquid will have a negligible effect on the vapour flow pattern which acts on the flowmeter. At the other extreme, it may be assumed that a mass flowmeter or a volume flowmeter measures correctly. In the first case the meter will provide the vapour flowrate, but provide no information about the liquid flowrate, in the second case, density may be required to give a full picture of the flow. If the dryness is known a correction factor can be applied (Miller, 1983).

1.7.4 Other potential multiphase flows

> Gas in solution in liquid
>   Gas–oil–ratio (GOR)
> High humidity
> Water droplets in air
> Cavitation
> Particulate matter

Liquids can contain gases in solution. For water the maximum amount is about 2 per cent by volume. The gas in solution does not increase the volume of the liquid by an equal amount since the gas molecules 'fit' in the 'gaps' in the liquid molecular structures. For hydrocarbons the amount of gas which can be held in solution is very large and the GOR (Gas–oil–ratio), which is the volume of gas at standard conditions to the volume of liquid can range up to 100 or more. In either case, but particularly the latter, changes in flow conditions, for instance a pressure drop, can cause the gas to come out of solution causing a two-phase flow.

High humidity has problems of a not dissimilar type. If high humidity exists with a consequent large amount of water vapour or other vapour, a change in conditions may result in the vapour changing to liquid droplets in the gas.

Cavitation may occur in certain liquid flows at pressures around ambient. Cavitation is the creation of vapour cavities within the liquid due to localised 'boiling' at low pressure. It can cause damage since the cavities can collapse very quickly and erode a solid surface. It can also cause errors in readings, since it results in a larger volume than for the liquid alone.

Particulate matter can cause wear as well as errors, and may need to be removed with a fine filter.

1.8 EXTREME FLOW CONDITIONS

> Very low flows $Re < 10^4$
> Very high flows $Re > 10^8$
> Corrosive fluids
> Fluids with low lubricity

We are sometimes required to measure very low flow rates or very high ones. Both of these extremes may cause problems. Very low flows ($Re < 10^4$) have a Reynolds number which may cause significant flow pattern changes. Very high flows ($Re > 10^8$) are so rare that we lack adequate information on their behaviour. We may also require a flowmeter capable of standing up to corrosive fluids. Certain fluids exhibit the characteristic of having very poor lubricating qualities; some flowmeters with rotating members will be particularly sensitive to such fluids. In these and other cases it will be necessary to obtain manufacturer's advice on suitability.

CHAPTER 2

Calibration

2.1 DATUM CONDITIONS

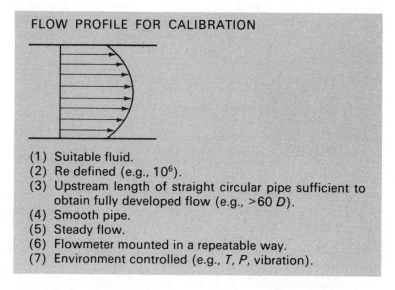

FLOW PROFILE FOR CALIBRATION

(1) Suitable fluid.
(2) Re defined (e.g., 10^6).
(3) Upstream length of straight circular pipe sufficient to obtain fully developed flow (e.g., >60 D).
(4) Smooth pipe.
(5) Steady flow.
(6) Flowmeter mounted in a repeatable way.
(7) Environment controlled (e.g., T, P, vibration).

The flow profile will affect the performance of most flowmeters. It is, therefore, essential that, for calibration, this is closely controlled. The above list contains those features which will cause the profile to be changed:

in shape;
in turbulence;
in time.

We must, therefore, ensure that we calibrate a flowmeter with this datum. This will require that we set the flowmeter in a straight length of smooth pipe (the maximum permitted roughness will probably be in the range $10^{-3}D$–$10^{-4}D$) sufficient to generate a fully developed profile without swirl. The fluid will need to be of a suitable type. This is particularly important with hydrocarbon flows where viscosity changes may introduce calibration changes.

Care should be taken over the concentricity of the flowmeters compared with the neighbouring pipework. Where high precision is sought it may be appropriate to position the flowmeter with spigots.

Flow steadiness is important since some meters are affected by unsteady flow and the unsteadiness may disturb the profile. Temperature and pressure variations can affect the viscosity of the fluid, as well as moving the calibration away from the datum. Vibration is known to affect certain meters more than others and should be avoided.

2.2   STEADY FLOW

ERRORS DUE TO UNSTEADY FLOW RESULT FROM:

(1) Non-linear flowmeter characteristics.
(2) Inertia of moving parts and fluid.
(3) Pulsation frequency close to operating frequency.
(4) Secondary equipment unsuitable for unsteady signals.

The need for a steady flow, while expected, is particularly important for non-linear flowmeters. In practice, almost all flowmeters are affected by unsteady flows. This is due to four main reasons.

(1) *Non-linear characteristic*   The differential pressure flowmeter, which essentially uses equation (1.24) (with an additional coefficient) has a quadratic characteristic, so that the mean pressure does not give the correct value of velocity. The same effect, but with more complex characteristics, may occur in other flowmeters.

(2) *Inertia*   The inertia of a turbine wheel spinning in a gas flow will make it very difficult for such a flowmeter to follow the flow. It will tend to over-read. Again, similar effects occur in other flowmeters.

(3) *Frequency of operation*   If the operating frequency of the flowmeter is close to that of the pulsations in the flow, then the flowmeter reading will be affected. An example of this is the vortex flowmeter, which has a tendency to 'lock on' to the pulsation frequency.

(4) *Secondary equipment*   Most flowmeters have a secondary system which converts the flowmeter signal to a readable quantity. The manometer is one example of this which can be seriously affected by unsteady flows.

2.3 CALIBRATION RIGS

FLOW CALIBRATION RIG
  – Standing start and stop.
  – Flying start and stop.
For a linear flowmeter standing start and stop may be satisfactory, if integration of the flow is available.

TYPES OF RIG

Gravimetric
  – mass of fluid in a measured time interval or total mass flowing through.

Volumetric
  – volume of fluid in a measured time interval or total volume flowing through.

Prover
  – swept volume of pipe by piston or sphere.

Transfer
  – transfer standard flowmeter in rig.

Having obtained a well-conditioned flow we need to measure it with precision. This requires either the measure of a certain volume passed in a measured time, or the mass passed in a measured time, or, for meters with sufficiently linear characteristics to give a total flow passed, the total volume or total mass may be sufficient, with flow stationary before and after. The meter prover offers an alternative method of achieving a volumetric calibration by using the swept volume as a close fitting sphere moves through a pipe between sensing switches. This method has been widely used in the oil industry to provide on-site calibration, for instance, of banks of turbine meters. The disadvantage of conventional provers is that they are very bulky. Recently, compact provers have been developed which appear to give good performance. A further option, of particular use in an organization needing precise calibrations, but unable to justify a full calibration rig, is to make use of a transfer standard flowmeter against which to calibrate their flowmeters.

The discussion which follows gives a brief review only of the main calibration methods. In particular, it does not attempt to review the methods in detail, as the reader who wishes to have a flowmeter calibrated will either send it to a recognized centre, or will seek advice from one of the centres (on page 144) on the construction of a suitable rig.

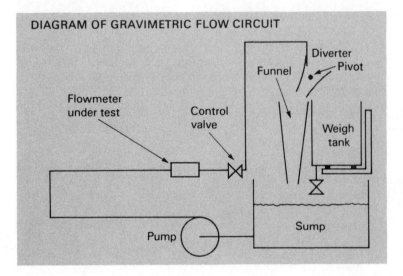

DIAGRAM OF GRAVIMETRIC FLOW CIRCUIT

Calibration rigs using a flying start and stop usually use water as the fluid. A diverter is used to switch the flow from the sump tank into a weighing tank for a timed period. Care is required in the design and adjustment of the diverter and timing switch, since it is virtually impossible to switch the flow from one tank to another instantaneously, and the timing switch must be adjusted to allow for the finite changeover time. The flow must be kept steady. This is traditionally achieved by a constant head tank, but is also commonly done with a closed loop with pump and sump tank. An interesting recent development is the use of a gyroscopic device to obtain the weight of water. The precession of the gyroscope is directly related to the torque created by the weight of the tank. The gravimetric method is commonly used for liquids, and, while usable for gases, becomes highly complex. A gas calibration rig using a gravimetric method is available at the National Engineering Laboratory (NEL), East Kilbride, Scotland.

The uncertainty achieved in the measurement of water flowrate by the UK primary standard at NEL is ± 0.1 per cent, and for the primary gas standard it is ± 0.25 per cent.

The volumetric method is widely used and is most convenient in standing

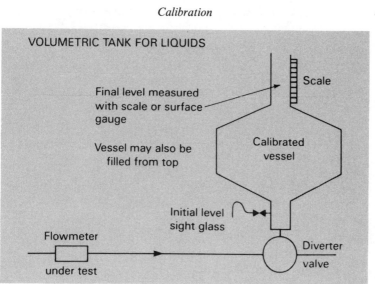

VOLUMETRIC TANK FOR LIQUIDS

Scale

Final level measured
with scale or surface
gauge

Calibrated
vessel

Vessel may also be
filled from top

Initial level
sight glass

Flowmeter

Diverter
valve

under test

start and stop mode. A large vessel is calibrated, for example using weighed quantities of distilled water at a known temperature. The top and bottom of the vessel are of small diameter so that small volume changes cause measurable level changes compared with the large volume contained in the centre portion of the vessel. The initial fluid level is measured, often by means of a sight glass and weir, and the vessel is filled with the liquid being metered. The final level is arranged to be within the slender top section where it can be measured precisely with a surface point gauge or with a rule attached to the outside of the vessel. Hence, the volume which has flowed is known and the reading of the meter being calibrated can be compared with it.

Proving vessels of this type are used to check meter calibrations to uncertainties within ± 0.1 per cent for custody transfer of hydrocarbon liquids. A typical vessel could be of 500 litres capacity. Such vessels, of various sizes, have also been used in the calibration of meters for milk.

Another type of volumetric rig makes use of the falling head method. A tall tank is filled with liquid. The liquid is allowed to flow through an outlet pipe to a flowmeter. The volume between two level switches is known and the meter is calibrated against this volume. The disadvantage of this method is that the flowrate will change slightly as the head falls.

The bell prover is a volumetric calibration device for gases, which also uses standing start and stop. It is particularly suitable for small domestic

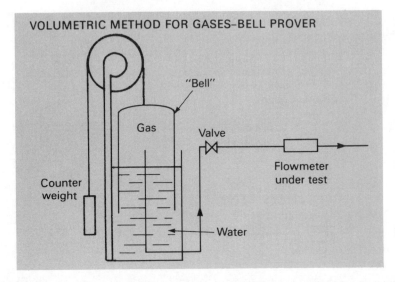

VOLUMETRIC METHOD FOR GASES–BELL PROVER

gas meters and is capable of achieving an uncertainty of as low as $\pm 0{\cdot}2$ per cent if particular care is taken. A similar approach allowing larger volumes of gas makes use of a large bag of precisely known volume.

The PVT method assumes a known relationship between pressure, volume, and temperature for the gas. The gas is contained in a large calibrated vessel for which the pressure and the temperature are precisely known. The gas is then allowed to flow through a heat exchanger, pressure control valve, and possibly a further regulator, before entering the meter under calibration. At the end of the calibration run, the volume of gas passed through the meter can be calculated from the change in the conditions in the calibrated vessel.

For very low flowrates of gas a method making use of the movement of a soap film through a vertically mounted burette is sometimes used.

Although the pipe prover has not been found satisfactory for gases, some recent developments in compact provers are more promising and may come into wider use in the future after evaluation by the relevant authorities.

The prover consists of a carefully constructed length of pipe. A unidirectional one is shown below. A sphere is projected into this pipe and its passage is recorded past two set points. The volume swept is known and the time taken is recorded. Other designs allow the sphere to pass both ways

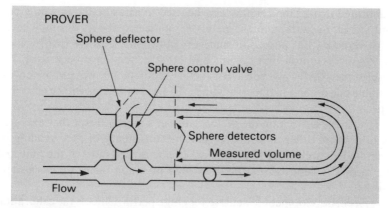

PROVER

Sphere deflector

Sphere control valve

Sphere detectors

Measured volume

Flow

(bi-directional). Instruments of this type are commonly included in hydrocarbon metering stations.

Conventional meter provers are very large and there are some applications where their space and weight may not be acceptable. For reasons such as these, a new generation of compact designs has recently appeared. These devices still depend on the swept volume of a tube, but use a piston and a very much reduced 'pipe' length. Thus, with great manufacturing precision it appears that the performance of these compact provers can rival that of the large pipe prover. One problem that arises in the use of these compact provers is the small amount of fluid which passes. Thus, if a flowmeter produces a pulse for a certain volume of fluid passed, the amount of pulses resulting from the fluid passed by a compact prover may be very low, causing a discrimination error. This has led to special techniques to overcome the problem, such as pulse interpolation.

The conventional pipe prover may achieve uncertainties of the order of 0·1 per cent or less with calibration, and compact provers will seek to achieve similar performances if they are to compete.

2.4 MASTER METERS

MASTER METERS
- Very high precision (e.g., positive displacement or turbine).
- Preferably operating in pairs to cross check.
- Preferably calibrated with upstream pipework and flow straightener.
- Provide a transfer standard from a Nationally certified rig.

Calibrated master meters may also be used to measure the flow in a pipe and, hence, to calibrate other meters. As indicated above, this may be the most economical option for some organizations. Positive displacement meters are common, but turbine and other meters have been used. For gases sonic nozzles provide a satisfactory method, and wet gas meters are suitable due to their high performance. These instruments will be described later.

To achieve a check on the performance of a master meter they are often used in pairs, either in series, so that the consistency of their readings is continually checked, or in parallel when one is used most of the time and the second is kept as a particularly high precision meter for occasional checks.

A recent development to achieve very high performance is the calibration of the meter with the upstream pipework and a flow straightener permanently in position, and the use of two of these packages in series. In this way any deviation caused by installation or by drift of one meter will appear as a relative shift in calibration between the two meters. Such meters or meter pairs are referred to as transfer standards, in that they allow a calibration standard to be transferred (with only a small increase in uncertainty) from a nationally certified rig to a manufacturer's rig or a research laboratory rig.

2.5   SITE CALIBRATIONS

Proving vessels
Pipe provers
Compact provers
Reference meters
Clamp-on meters
Probes
Tracers
Inspection and measurement
Self-checking systems

Site calibration is valuable, in that it takes account of installation effects, but in many cases it is very difficult to achieve with a low value of uncertainty.

Proving vessels, pipe provers, compact provers, and reference meters may be suitable for use in many petroleum product installations, where suitable connections are available. Uncertainties in the order of 0.2 per cent and better are achievable.

Clamp-on meters (ultrasonic), probes, and tracers may be used. However, they require considerable expertise and care to achieve a calibration which is unlikely to be better than 1 per cent.

Inspection and dimensional measurement of installed flowmeters depends either on standard instruments (differential pressure) or good historical documentation from original calibration and installation.

Some systems may be designed as self-checking either by redirecting the flow to a second (master) meter or by using flowmeters with a self-checking function.

2.6 GENERAL COMMENTS

For a calibration to be acceptable, the ultimate source of the measurement must be known and the calibration must be *traceable* to that standard. Thus, in the UK, the national standard for liquid measurement is held by the National Engineering Laboratory, and that for gas by the Department of Energy, Gas and Oil Measurement Branch, Leicester, England. These standards are themselves traceable back to more fundamental measures of mass, time, and volume. As a result of this a traceability chain is formed. Each link is formed from a rig or flowmeter calibrated against a rig or flowmeter of greater precision, with sufficient frequency to ensure continuing confidence. It is clear, therefore, that if a transfer standard with an uncertainty of, say, ±0.25 per cent is used to calibrate a flowmeter, the uncertainty in the calibration of that flowmeter will be greater than ±0.25 per cent.

It can be seen from the discussion above that the calibration uncertainties achievable at present are of the order of:

for liquids   0.1 per cent
for gases   0.25 per cent

Where total mass or volume, rather than flowrate, is required, these values may be improved.

CHAPTER 3

Selection

CONSIDERATIONS
- Type of fluid.
- Special fluid constraints.
- Flowmeter constraints.
- Environmental considerations.
- Total cost.

For the next few chapters we shall be discussing the operation, advantages, and disadvantages of the most common meters available commercially or (in the case of the differential pressure meters) able to be manufactured by a prospective user. Some readers may read later chapters for general interest. Most will probably have a specific application in mind and will want to be guided to the instruments most appropriate to it. This chapter attempts to guide, recognizing that the uninitiated will be looking for sufficient knowledge to deal intelligently with manufacturers and their brochures, and that the initiated will probably have by-passed this introductory book.

In the limited scope of this text it is not possible to be exhaustive about the many facets of flow measurement and flow meters which one needs to take into account in making a selection. An attempt has been made here to focus on the more general considerations leaving the particular to the manufacturer to supply relative to his design.

The table at the end of this chapter concentrates on the main types of meter. For convenience they are subdivided into momentum, volume, and mass sensing meters. This subdivision also emphasises that, for instance, a meter which responds to momentum will be sensitive to density change. Where a less common meter of the same family has particular features which make it unique or particularly useful in certain applications, these may be indicated in notes in the table and in the discussion in subsequent chapters, where other points arising from this chapter will be elaborated.

3.1 NATURE OF THE FLUID TO BE METERED

TYPE OF FLUID
- liquid or gas
- slurry
- multi-phase

The first choice, liquid or gas, is the most obvious, and will cause a few types of meter to be eliminated, although most of the main types have designs suitable for one or the other. Increasingly, there is interest in the measurement of slurries and two- (or more) phase flows. The selection of suitable meters for these is severely restricted at present. In the table x indicates unsuitable and an * indicates suitable except where some are more suitable (**) than others. A ? indicates that it is not common, but might be appropriate, in this application.

The result is rather subjective, as will become apparent as each meter is considered. For instance, the electromagnetic flowmeter has found a valuable role in slurry flow measurement and is almost unique in this. However, the coriolis mass flowmeter is claimed to be suitable for slurry, and an ultrasonic flowmeter has been specially designed for this purpose. The electromagnetic flowmeter is also useful in two-phase flows when the continuous phase is conducting. However, venturis are usable, but with great caution. A note in the table indicates that the ultrasonic correlation flowmeter and the doppler flow monitor may also be worth considering in such flows.

SPECIAL FLUID CONSTRAINTS
- clean or dirty
- hygienic
- corrosive
- abrasive
- high flammability
- low lubricity
- fluids causing scaling

In addition, and after initial selection of the most likely types, it will be necessary to discuss with manufacturers special fluids.

Resulting constraints will vary according to materials and design details and will not necessarily be related to a particular flowmeter design. However, flowmeters with rotating parts will be less suitable for dirty, abrasive, or low lubricity fluids. Abrasion may also detract from the performance of other meters, such as the vortex meter.

An additional constraint is that the liquid must be conducting for the application of an electromagnetic flowmeter.

3.2   FLOWMETER CONSTRAINTS

FLOWMETER CONSTRAINTS
- Precision.
- Diameter range.
- Temperature range.
- Pressure maximum.
- Viscosity range.
- Flow range.
- Pressure loss created by the flowmeter.
- Sensitivity to installation.
- Sensitivity to pulsation.
- Whether the flowmeter has a clear bore.
- Whether a clamp-on version is available.
- Response time.
- Ambient conditions required.

Apart from the initial cost of the flowmeter, which is considered last, the main considerations will be as shown in the box above.

Precision is perhaps the most difficult to determine, since both user and manufacturer are prone to overstate their requirements and capabilities. In the table:

   ***   is for random error < 0.1 per cent
    **   is for random error < 0.5 per cent
     *   is for random error < 2 per cent

The estimates are the author's view of the precision of flowmeters. They are values which should be achievable with a particular type of flowmeter. For a standard orifice the uncertainty before calibration due to the discharge coefficient is 0.6 per cent to 0.75 per cent. After calibration the total uncertainty will be less than this, and it is reasonable to assume that the random error will be less than 0.5 per cent. This appears to be confirmed by data. Some manufacturers may feel able to claim higher values, but the reader should ask for justification for such claims. For instance, some manufacturers claim that a single beam ultrasonic flowmeter is capable of a random error less than 0·5 per cent. However, this performance needs adequate substantiation before being accepted. Several other commercial flowmeter designs have claims of better than 0·5 per cent, but again this should be viewed with scepticism, since it indicates a level of precision which is very hard to achieve. Some manufacturers may not always achieve the values indicated. The repeatability of a variable area meter is often quoted as a percentage of full scale and so on balance is just outside the * rating.

Precision relates to random error. It does not allow for changes in bias error due to changes in method of measurement, location, or long elapsed times. Thus, if the reader is concerned about reproducibility or total uncertainty, these estimates may not provide the most appropriate guide. Where possible some attempt has been made in the discussion of some meters to indicate the possibility of drift over a six month period.

Diameter, temperature, and flow are the author's best estimates based on manufacturers' literature, and the general references at the end of the book. In all cases the diligent reader can probably find examples of greater ranges than those given, and manufacturers are always seeking to extend the capability of their instruments. Note that in the column for flow range, the values in parentheses indicate kg/h rather than m^3/h. The table on page 3 has a conversion in terms of water flow.

The maximum pressure has not been included since, apart from exceptionally high pressure applications, when one might turn to an orifice plate or a turbine meter, there appear to be versions of most designs which are offered for normal industrial ranges. In some cases minimum pressures may be important, as cavitation may be a danger, and the manufacturer should be consulted.

The pressure loss is given as H (high), M (medium), or L (low). Only the electromagnetic and ultrasonic meters have been categorized as L, and for each there is virtually no more pressure loss than in a similar length of pipe. The orifice plate and target are H, and positive displacement (PD) and vortex are H/M, although their relative losses will depend on such things as the instrumentation being driven by the PD meter.

The positive displacement meter may be assumed to be insensitive to upstream installation effects and is, therefore, rated L. Most other flowmeters are affected and these have been categorised for a fitting, such as a bend, at 5–10 D upstream.

L　Negligible effect

M　<2 per cent increase in uncertainty

H　>2 per cent increase in uncertainty

All of the categorizations are best estimates by the author, and manufacturers may be prepared to uprate them.

The behaviour of variable area and coriolis meters is based on the assumption that the flow direction change normally associated with their inlet piping will reduce sensitivity to other upstream fittings, but there is some suggestion that the coriolis meters are not entirely unaffected by inlet flow profile.

Data on pulsation effects is too inadequate to make any useful categorization. Most flowmeters are sensitive to pulsation over part of their range, with the possible exception of the ultrasonic flowmeter and the viscous flowmeter, which was specially designed to cope with pulsating gas flows.

The flowmeters with essentially a clear bore (non-intrusive) are the electromagnetic and ultrasonic types. The only flowmeter which may fail and block the line is the positive displacement flowmeter. All the others have a partial line blockage, although the venturi has such a smooth change in section that its effect is probably of small concern.

Only the ultrasonic flowmeter family offer clamp-on options (non-invasive).

If a high speed of response is required this may eliminate some designs (for instance, for control installations where a response in less than a second may be required).

Finally the compatibility of the flowmeter and its related instrumentation to the ambient conditions should be checked with the manufacturer.

3.3　ENVIRONMENT

ENVIRONMENTAL CONSIDERATIONS
- Ambient temperature.
- Humidity.
- Exposure to weather, etc.
- Level of electromagnetic radiation.
- Vibration.
- Classification of the area requiring explosion proof, intrinsic safety, etc.

The installation of the flowmeter will also be affected by environmental considerations. These will need to be assessed in consultation with particular manufacturers. Virtually all commercial designs are capable of withstanding or meeting all these environmental considerations and most manufacturers will offer particular versions to cope with particular constraints. One apparent exception to this (at present) is vibration which may affect, for example, coriolis meters.

3.4 SPECIAL EFFECTS

Under certain circumstances cavitation can occur in a liquid, gas or air may be entrained in the liquid, and droplets can form in a saturated vapour. In addition, some flows may be particularly abrasive. These needs will again be assessed in conjunction with the manufacturer, or with experts from whom advice may be sought.

3.5 PRICE

This is possibly the most important consideration and is difficult to tabulate since the range of price for any design is wide and the datum is always changing! The author has, therefore, attempted to rate the initial cost of the flowmeters as H (high), M (medium), or L (low). However, the medium bracket tends to become a 'catch-all' and covers, for instance, electro-magnetic, turbine, and vortex flowmeters, which can actually have an initial cost range of 4:1 for a 100 mm diameter design. For this reason L/M or M/H have been used where low or high cost versions are available.

3.6 CHOOSING

Until an expert system is available, flowmeter selection will be an iterative procedure between the user and the manufacturer. The object of a book such as this, or the other books listed in the bibliography, some of which are very detailed, is to aid the user in making the initial selection, and to educate him or her sufficiently to be able to ask the manufacturer the right questions. If, say, a mass flowmeter is definitely required, then the selection is reduced. But, even so, the option of combining a momentum, or a volume sensitive flowmeter with a density cell should not be overlooked, and may be an option which offers greater confidence.

The first column of the following table is a partial list of the types of flowmeter available, and the next three columns can be used to eliminate those which are clearly inapplicable.

1	2	3	4	5	6	7	8
Flowmeter type	Liquid or gas	Slurry	Other two-phase	Precision	Diameter range[3] (mm)	Temperature range (°C)[4]	Flow range[4] (m^3/hr (kg/hr))
Momentum[1]		†	†	†			
Orifice	L / G	x	?	**	50–1000	up to +540	1–3×10^6 (L) 10–4×10^6 (G)
Venturi	L / G	*	*	**	50–1200	−180 to +540	30–7000 (L) 400–10^5 (G)
Target	L / G	?²	*	*	12–100	−45 to +540	1–5×10^4(L) 0·5– (G)
Variable area	L / G	x	x		15–150	−200 to +350	10^{-3}–1000 (L) 10^{-4}–2000 (G)
Volume							
Positive displacement	L / G	x	?²	***	4–1000	−50 to +315 (L) −50– +120 (G)	0·01–2000 (L) 0·01–3000 (G)
Turbine	L / G	x	x	***	5–600	−200 to +260	0·01–10 000 (L) 0·01–10^5 (G)
Vortex	L / G	x	x	**	12–200	−40 to +200	3–2000 (L) 50–10^5 (G)
Electromagnetic	L	**	**	**	2–3000	−50 to +190	10^{-2}–3×10^5
Ultrasonic transit time	L / G	?²	?²	*	3–3000 (L) 20–2000 (G)	−40 to +200	3–3×10^5 (L) 3–10^6 (G)
Mass							
Thermal	G	x	x	*	3–6	0 to +65	3×10^{-4}–0·03
Wheatstone Bridge	L	x	x	**	6–60	−50 to +150	($0\cdot05$–$2\cdot5 \times 10^4$)
Angular momentum	L	x	x	**	20–30	−40 to +150	(100–5×10^3)
Coriolis	L	*	x	**	1–150	−75 to +245	(5–5×10^5)

† *** Very high; ** more suitable/high; * Suitable/medium; ?/blank Uncertain/lower; x Unsuitable.
‡ L = Low; M = Medium; H = High.

Notes
[1] Some proprietary devices offer special features: higher differential pressure, linear characteristic, suitable for pulsating flows, etc.
[2] Observe specific constraints for each type of meter: installed life, solids limits, material compatibility, etc.
[3] Larger or smaller sizes may be available.
[4] Other ranges may be available.
[5] Flow conditioning may be used in some applications to reduce this effect.

9	10	11	
Pressure loss	*Sensitivity to installation*[5]	*Initial cost*	*Notes*
‡	‡	‡	
H	H	L/M	Concentric ISO orifice with differential pressure cell assumed. Eccentric used for two-phase flow.
M	M/L	M/H	
H	H	M	
M	L	L	Glass/plastic assumed; higher ratings for steel.
H/M	L	H	
M	H	L/M	Assumes high precision instruments rather than robust water meters, etc. Pelton wheel for very low flows.
H/M	H	L/M	Fluidic flowmeter suitable for very low flows.
L	M	M	Only available commercially for electrically conducting liquids.
L	M/H	M/H	Single beam design are more sensitive to installation. Correlation and Doppler for two-phase flows.
M	L	M	Available as a by-pass flowmeter for higher flows (up to 400 m^3/h). Low flow liquid versions available.
n/a	L	H	Specialist instrument more suitable for R & D laboratory
M	M	M	Particularly suitable for aircraft fuel flow.
M	M/L	H	

Column 5 will, in most cases, only allow one or two instruments to be eliminated unless very high precision is required.

Columns 6–8 can be used to eliminate further by excluding those which do not meet the requirements of the particular application. Again for most applications this will not remove many flowmeters.

Column 9 may be a critical consideration in a few applications, but since orifice plates with high pressure loss dominate industrial flow measurement, it is unlikely that pressure loss will be an overriding consideration. However, with greater energy conservation this may influence the final choice.

Column 10 may be of greater importance, as in many applications the installation options are limited and the meter may have to be installed in a very short length of straight pipe. In this situation upstream pipe fittings may affect the meter reading. If a meter with high sensitivity to flow profile distortion has to be used, some improvement may be achieved by installing a flow conditioner, but this must be done with care, may add to the pressure drop in the line, and may cause an unacceptable obstruction.

Column 11 can be no more than an indication of broad ranges of initial cost. Thus, if this is a dominant factor, and budget is restricted, then a variable area device may be the only option. There are other aspects of cost which have not been mentioned. Initial cost will, of course, include both purchase price and costs of installation. There will also be ongoing costs associated with maintenance, energy loss due to the presence of the flowmeter, and savings due to the information which the flowmeter provides. If the flowmeter is clearly required, then the savings should outweigh the costs. This does not reduce the responsibility of the user to install the best and most economical instrument for the job!

CHAPTER 4

Momentum Flowmeters

STANDARD INSTRUMENTS
 – Orifice plate.
 – Venturi meter.
 – Nozzles.

OTHER PRESSURE SENSING DEVICES
 – Special orifice plates.
 – Sonic nozzle.
 – Proprietary designs.

OTHER MOMENTUM SENSING DEVICES
 – Drag plate/Target meter.
 – Rotameter/Float-in-tube.

In this chapter we consider flowmeters which sense the momentum of the flow, the most important of which are the differential pressure devices. It is appropriate to take the differential pressure flowmeters first, since they have a long and distinguished history and still dominate the flow measurement scene despite many alternative methods. The reasons for this dominance can be attributed to:

a traditional conservatism, which trusts the known device despite its shortcomings rather than the unknown device;

a wealth of experience which has been distilled into BS 1042 and ISO 5167 allowing a flowmeter of known precision to be designed and constructed by a well-founded flow laboratory;

a (mistaken) view that it is a simple and cheap matter to design and build a flowmeter of 'high accuracy'. It isn't, but that is a later part of the story.

The flow through the venturi illustrates the well-behaved nature of a flow when the area changes blend reasonably smoothly from one size to another. Converging flow is particularly well behaved, while diverging flow for diffusion of small enough angle will continue to remain generally in one direction. As the flow rate increases due to the smaller area, so the pressure

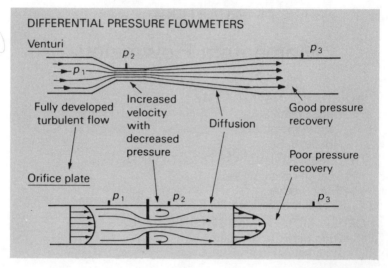

decreases, and vice versa. However, 'pressure recovery' is dependent on the smoothness of the expanding flow.

In contrast, the flow through the orifice plate is far from smooth. The abrupt area change caused by the orifice plate, while causing the flow to contract as it passes through the orifice, will also cause a small recirculation zone in the corner upstream of the plate and a large recirculation zone downstream of the plate around the central jet area. In addition to this the flow downstream of the plate is highly disturbed and the diffusion will result in high pressure losses.

The venturi meter was invented by Clemens Herschel (1842–1930), a graduate of Harvard University, and he named it after Venturi in recognition of his important research on the device. Physically it illustrates some important ideas of the differential device. Because it has a tapered inlet converging from Station 1 to Station 2 the losses in the flow are very small and equation (1.24) gives a good estimate of the velocity in the main pipe based on the pressure difference, Δp.

$$V_1 = \frac{m}{\sqrt{(1-m^2)}} \sqrt{\left(\frac{2\Delta p}{\rho}\right)} \tag{1.24}$$

where $m = d^2/D^2$, D is the main pipe diameter, and d is the throat diameter. By using a tapered diffuser the flow is caused to diffuse with less loss than results from a sudden expansion, but there will still be some loss of total pressure between p_1 and p_3. We will return to the venturi meter after considering the orifice meter – the most common of the differential pressure (DP) meters.

However, it is appropriate to note at this point that ρ, the density, appears in the equation, confirming that, since these meters sense momentum, it is necessary also to obtain a value of the density.

4.1   ORIFICE PLATE METER

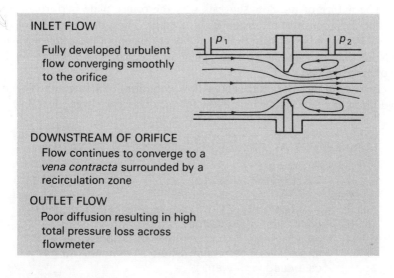

INLET FLOW

Fully developed turbulent flow converging smoothly to the orifice

DOWNSTREAM OF ORIFICE

Flow continues to converge to a *vena contracta* surrounded by a recirculation zone

OUTLET FLOW

Poor diffusion resulting in high total pressure loss across flowmeter

The orifice plate flowmeter is the most common industrial instrument. It is apparently simple to construct and has a great weight of experience to confirm its operation. However, it causes a complex flow pattern compared with the smooth venturi flow.

The inlet flow will almost always be fully developed turbulent if adequate upstream pipe length is allowed and the international and national standards are followed (ISO 5167 and BS 1042). In the following description the design with pressure tappings at one diameter, D, upstream of the orifice plate, and half a diameter, $D/2$, downstream is considered. The upstream wall pressure tapping senses the pressure essentially before any redistribution of the flow occurs. This flow converges to the orifice and continues to converge to the *vena contracta*, the narrowest point of the submerged jet, downstream of the orifice. Outside this position is a recirculation region across which the pressure is sensed at the wall. The flow downstream of this point is disturbed and pressure recovery is much less efficient than in the venturi meter. The resulting pressure loss across the flowmeter is much greater than for the venturi meter.

Were we able to measure the diameter of this *vena contracta*, equation (1.24) could be used as a reasonable approximation to the relationship between flowrates and pressure drop. Recognizing that this is not easily obtainable, a discharge coefficient is used.

The nature of the flow suggests why the orifice plate performance is particularly sensitive to certain design details. Thus, the sharpness of the plate leading edge is likely to affect the development of the *vena contracta*. (Note that the standard orifice plate is bevelled, if necessary, on its downstream side.)

Because of the losses in the actual flow, equation (1.24) is modified by the addition of coefficients which allow for the divergence from ideal flow.

DIFFERENTIAL PRESSURE FLOWMETER EQUATION

The mass flowrate
$$q_m = C \, E \, \varepsilon (\pi/4) d^2 \sqrt{(2\rho_1 \Delta p)} \qquad (4.1)$$
where

E = $1/\sqrt{(1-\beta^4)} = 1/\sqrt{(1-m^2)}$ where $\beta = d/D$ and $m = d^2/D^2$

C = coefficient of discharge

ε = expansibility factor (= 1 for incompressible fluids and allows a correction where a flowmeter for gas is calibrated with water)

d = orifice diameter

D = upstream pipe diameter

Δp = differential pressure

ρ_1 = density at the upstream pressure tapping

The differential pressure flowmeter equation is given in BS 1042 and ISO 5167, and an expression is given for the coefficient of discharge, C. The coefficient allows for the very different flow in the orifice plate as compared with an ideal contracting flow, and, in particular, allows for the size of the *vena contracta* compared with the orifice.

COEFFICIENT OF DISCHARGE for D and $D/2$ tapping

$$C = 0.5959 + 0.0312\beta^{2.1} - 0.1840\beta^8 + 0.0029\beta^{2.5}\left(\frac{10^6}{Re}\right)^{0.75}$$

$$+0.0390\beta^4(1-\beta^4)^{-1} - 0.0337 \times 0.47\beta^3 \qquad (4.2)$$

If

$d \geqslant 12.5$ mm: 50 mm $\leqslant D \leqslant 760$ mm: $0.2 \leqslant \beta \leqslant 0.75$:
$1260\beta^2 D \leqslant Re \leqslant 10^8$ (D in mm)
then
Uncertainty in C for $\beta \leqslant 0.6$ is 0.6%
for $0.6 \leqslant \beta \leq 0.75$ is $\beta\%$

The expression recommended (by ISO 5167 and BS 1042) for C, for D and $D/2$ tappings is given above (the Stolz equation). Note, however, that this may only be used with confidence provided certain constraints are met on d, D, β, and Re. Outside these limits the standards give no authority for its use. Within these limits the value of C is said to have an uncertainty of at best 0·6 per cent. An updated form of this equation will shortly be available.

The coefficient of discharge for orifice plates with corner and flange taps is similar to that above, except that the last two terms are modified and the limits of use are changed. Because of the easier installation, corner and flange taps are widely used.

The expansibility factor is briefly defined above, and provides an adjustment factor to allow differential pressure devices to be calibrated on incompressible water for use on compressible gas. The problems of achieving high accuracy when metering gas are considerable since the density will vary through the orifice meter.

The pressure loss across the meter is given as

$$\Delta p_{loss} \simeq \frac{1 - CE\beta^2}{1 + CE\beta^2} \Delta p \qquad (4.3)$$

Taking: $C \simeq 0.6$; $E \simeq 1$; $\beta \simeq 0.5$, shows that only about 30 per cent of the pressure reduction, Δp, is recovered downstream of the meter.

It is important to appreciate the constraints set out in the standards. These must be respected if the uncertainty values are to be used with any authority. Thus, some examples of the manufacturing constraints on the orifice plate meter are given below. The orifice plate is not a simple device from which high accuracy is automatically obtained. The attainment of high accuracy is only as a result of careful observation of the correct design procedures and manufacturing requirements.

ORIFICE PLATE – MANUFACTURE, PRECISION, AND INSTALLATION

Examples of manufacturing constraints:
Flat to within 1%
plate thickness to within 0·001 D
Upstream edge radius $\leqslant 0\cdot 0004\ d$
downstream pressure tapping position for $\beta \leqslant 0\cdot 6$ to ±0·02 D.
Examples of installation constraints (add 0·5% uncertainty for parenthesized numbers).

		Upstream diameters		Downstream diameters
β	90° bend	2×90° bends in ⊥ planes	Gate valve fully open	All
0·2	10 (6)	34 (17)	12 (6)	4 (2)
0·5	14 (7)	40 (20)	12 (6)	6 (3)
0·8	46 (23)	80 (40)	30 (15)	8 (4)

Example β=0·5 90° bend 10 D Upstream
Uncertainty 0·6%+0·5%=1·1%

Even if the meter is made to standard specification its performance may be reduced by poor installation. The table gives a few values from the standard, and it is clear from these that very long straight sections of pipe are required to retain the uncertainties set out earlier. For a β of 0·8 downstream of two bends in perpendicular planes a straight run of at least 88 diameters is required (allowing for both upstream and downstream lengths). An additional uncertainty is added of 0·5 per cent for lengths down to the parenthesized values.

Thus the example given of an orifice plate installed with a β=0·5 10 D downstream of a bend results in a total uncertainty of 1·1 per cent for the meter, apart from errors due to the other parameters in equation (4.1) and the pressure measurement. To achieve a lower uncertainty it is necessary to have the orifice meter calibrated at a suitable laboratory.

We have concentrated on orifice plates with D and $D/2$ tappings. Orifice plates are commonly used with corner and flange tappings rather than D and $D/2$ tappings, and requirements are detailed in the standards. In addition some orifice plates for special applications have eccentric or semi-circular orifices.

ADVANTAGES OF ORIFICE PLATES
- Well defined and documented.
- Based on long experience.
- Uncertainty calculable.
- Straight-forward to install.

DISADVANTAGES
- Non-linear.
- High pressure loss.
- Very sensitive to installation effects.
- Very careful construction required to obtain calculable uncertainty.
- Small usable range.
- Pulsation errors due to square law.

The summary above highlights the factors already discussed. The orifice (together with the venturi and the nozzles) is the only flowmeter which can be constructed from standard design guides, and these are based on much greater experience than is available for any other flowmeter. Although the uncertainty is not as low as some have assumed, it is calculable with reasonable confidence. The orifice can be installed between flanges – a feature which some modern flowmeters are attempting to emulate.

Some of its disadvantages such as high pressure loss and sensitivity to installation are lessened in the venturi meter. Its range is restricted for a particular orifice size by the constraints of differential pressure measurement, and great care must be taken in construction and installation. It will also require careful maintenance to ensure that the initial geometry is retained. Unless coupled with a fast response pressure measurement system it will be particularly subject to pulsation error due to the squared term in the flowmeter equation.

APPLICATION
- Almost any single phase Newtonian flow (for high viscosity fluids a quadrant or conical orifice may be used).
- Unsuitable for abrasive fluids.
- Use with caution in two-phase fluids.

COST – Medium (allowing for installation using pressure transducer etc.).

There are probably few single phase flows for which an orifice has not been used at some time. The standards require that the fluid is physically and thermally homogeneous and of single phase. However, highly dispersed colloidal solutions such as milk are allowed by the standard.

For very viscous flows it may be appropriate to use a quadrant or a conical orifice. Abrasive fluids will, apart from other effects, wear the orifice plate and cause a change in discharge coefficient.

If the orifice is used in a two-phase flow it will be outside the standard requirements and should be used with caution and with suitable bleed holes to remove liquid or gas from the upstream face of the orifice plate.

The cost of manufacture and installation is increased by the need to check dimensional correctness before installation. In addition the pressure leads and the differential pressure cells must be correctly installed to allow filling, bleeding, seal liquid, etc., as required by the fluid and installation.

4.2   VENTURI METER

VENTURI TUBE – STANDARD DESIGN

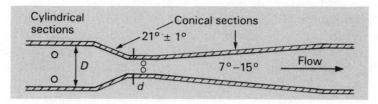

DISCHARGE COEFFICIENT

Type of convergent	Constraints	C	Uncertainty in C (%)
Rough cast	100 mm $\leqslant D \leqslant$ 800 mm $0.3 \leqslant \beta \leqslant 0.75$ $2 \times 10^5 \leqslant \mathrm{Re} \leqslant 2 \times 10^6$	0.984	0.7
Machined	50 mm $\leqslant D \leqslant$ 250 mm $0.4 \leqslant \beta \leqslant 0.75$ $2 \times 10^5 \leqslant \mathrm{Re} \leqslant 1 \times 10^6$	0.995	1.0
Rough welded sheet iron	200 mm $\leqslant D \leqslant$ 1200 mm $0.4 \leqslant \beta \leqslant 0.7$ $2 \times 10^5 \leqslant \mathrm{Re} \leqslant 2 \times 10^6$	0.985	1.5

The standard design of venturi is shown above with requirements on size of cone angles. Other details may be obtained from the standards (ISO 5167 and BS 1042). Although the venturi performance approximates to the ideal of equation (1.24), it is still necessary to introduce a discharge coefficient, C. The effect on C of the reduced losses in the flow is apparent from the value of C which for the machined version is only 0.5 per cent from the ideal Bernoulli prediction. The values of the uncertainties in C are related to the available data and the precision of the geometrical definition; to achieve a lower value it will be necessary to have the venturi meter calibrated. The pressure loss from this device is likely to lie between 5 and 20 per cent of the measured differential pressure. The throat and adjacent curvature must have a roughness less than 0.00001 of the throat diameter. For other finishes the reader should refer to the standards.

The effect of upstream pipe fittings on the performance of the venturi is much reduced from the orifice requirements, presumably because of the much greater flow stability in the venturi. Thus a 90 degree bend at 5 D or more upstream should not affect the meter's performance. A gate valve fully open, an expander, and a reducer will require increasing lengths of upstream pipe separating them from the meter to retain its performance, while two bends in perpendicular planes introducing swirl will add an additional uncertainty value. It is also necessary to consider the effects of the pipework upstream of the disturbing fitting and to consult the standards on the precautions which should be taken.

ADVANTAGES RELATIVE TO THE ORIFICE
- Lower pressure loss than orifice.
- Less affected by upstream flow distortion.

DISADVANTAGES
- Low differential pressure.
- Higher initial costs than orifice.
- Length of meter.

We have noted above the level of the pressure loss, and this may be an important consideration in some applications. The reduced sensitivity to upstream fittings may also be important, although this is offset by the greater initial length of the venturi.

An additional advantage might be seen as the high value of discharge coefficient, which means that the performance approaches the theoretical value, and this, in turn, could suggest a more reliable precision.

The venturi has two major disadvantages. It is expensive to construct and it has a large axial length which may be unacceptable in certain applications. For this reason various other differential pressure devices are covered in the standard which attempt to achieve a compromise between the convenience of the orifice plate and the performance of the venturi.

TYPICAL APPLICATIONS
- Water supply measurement.
- Large flows (to conserve energy).
- Slurry and multiphase flows.

COST – Medium to high.

Where energy conservation is an important consideration in large pumped flows, the low head loss of the venturi becomes attractive. It has been used for slurry and two-phase flows for which some data is available, but it should be applied with caution to such flows.

The initial cost is higher than the orifice, since it is a much larger device to make.

4.3 SPECIAL ORIFICE PLATES AND FLOW NOZZLES

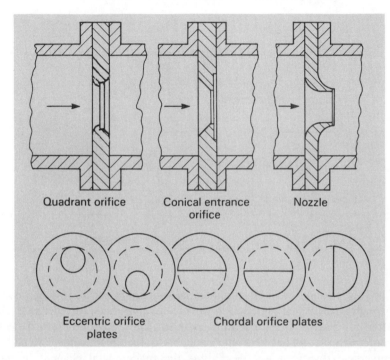

Quadrant orifice   Conical entrance   Nozzle
                    orifice

Eccentric orifice   Chordal orifice plates
plates

Apart from the orifice designs in the standards which have been discussed above, there are orifices with quadrant and conical inlets for viscous fluids, and there are also eccentric and chordal plates which are more suited to two-phase flows, since they allow the second phase to pass by suitably orientating the orifice. Data on these devices is available in some of the references in the bibliography.

Several nozzle designs are available in the standards which achieve a smooth and well-controlled flow contraction and avoid the problems of the sensitivity of the *vena contracta* to extraneous parameters. In these, the downstream pressure is sensed by flange tappings or similar, but the throat is well defined by the nozzle design. They are more stable than the orifice for high temperatures and high velocities, experiencing less wear and being less likely to distort. They are particularly applicable in steam flows. To approach the low loss of the venturi without its length, a venturi nozzle is available with a divergent region which improves pressure recovery.

4.4 SONIC NOZZLE (OR CRITICAL NOZZLE)

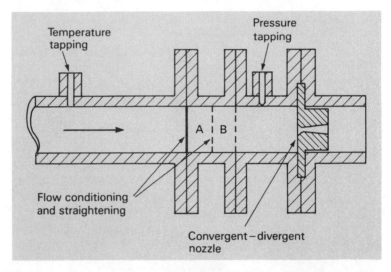

The flow is conditioned by straightening vanes at A and B. It then passes through a perforated plate which will create an artificial turbulence level. After this plate it enters a settling chamber. Thus, any flow disturbances from upstream will have become negligible by the time the flow enters the convergent–divergent nozzle. This is the fundamental element in the system. The area of flow here is much smaller than in the settling region. The key feature of the nozzle is that it is unaffected by downstream changes provided it is operating critically. The theory of compressible flow of a gas through a convergent–divergent passage shows that, for a sufficiently low back pressure, the velocity at the throat, or narrowest point in the duct, becomes sonic, that is, the Mach number becomes unity. Because information in a gas is carried by very small pressure waves, sonic conditions at the throat prevent transmission of information from downstream. The flow is said to be choked under these conditions and changes downstream of the nozzle will not affect the flow upstream of the nozzle throat. The nozzle for this reason can also be used as a flow control as well as a flowmeter, and it is often convenient to combine these roles

PRACTICAL FLOWMETER EQUATION

$$q_m = \frac{A^* C \, C^* p_0}{\sqrt{\{(\bar{R}/M)T_0\}}} \tag{4.4}$$

A^* is the throat area.
The discharge coefficient, C, is obtained from experimental data. C^*, the critical flow function, becomes C_i^* for a perfect gas where

$$C_i^* = \sqrt{\gamma} \left(\frac{2}{\gamma+1} \right)^{\frac{\gamma+1}{2(\gamma-1)}} \tag{4.5}$$

For a real gas, C^* is obtained from tables and formulae.
p_0 and T_0 are upstream stagnation conditions.
$\bar{R}$ is the universal gas constant.
M is the molecular weight.

The equation defining the performance of the sonic nozzle, although empirical, is very closely related to the equation obtained from one-dimensional compressible flow theory. It is important to note that the mass flow of the gas through the nozzle is directly proportional to the pressure in the upstream chamber, provided the temperature remains constant. It is, thus, essentially, a linear mass flowmeter for gases. The equation from one-dimensional flow theory is modified by the addition of a discharge coefficient which is empirically obtained and incorporated in a draft international standard document. The form given below is for toroidal throat venturi nozzles. Other values are available for cylindrical throat venturi nozzles.

DISCHARGE COEFFICIENT C

$$C = a - b/Re_d^{-n} \tag{4.6}$$

Re_d range	a	b	n	Source
10^5–10^7	0·9935(4)	1·525	0·5	ISO draft
4×10^4–3×10^6	0·99738	3·058	0·5	Arnberg *et al.*
3×10^5–10^7	0·99103	0·0	—	Brain and Reid

ISO uncertainty $\pm 0·5\%$ with 95% confidence level.

The value of C^* may be obtained from reference books (Miller, 1983). Its value is given for a perfect gas above. (Re_d is the Reynolds number based on the throat diameter.)

PRECISION
– random error probably less than ±0·3%.
UNCERTAINTY
– Allowing for all measurements, ±1–1·5% (without calibration).
INSTALLATION
– Unaffected due to smoothing and settling chamber.

The draft ISO standard lays down design details to ensure that the predicted performance is achieved. The uncertainty of the instrument depends on uncertainties of all the parameters in the equation, but is likely to lie in the range $\pm 1 - \pm 1.5$ per cent. Precision is likely to be such as to allow an uncertainty after calibration of the order of ± 0.3 per cent.

The installation of the device with gauzes and settling chamber is such that upstream fittings should have a negligible effect. It would also appear that upstream pulsation should average correctly.

ADVANTAGES
– It provides a transfer standard for gas mass flowrate.
– It is unaffected by downstream changes.
– The upstream stagnation pressure is directly proportional to the mass flow for constant stagnation temperature, etc.
DISADVANTAGES
– It will not easily cope with a wide range of flow.
– It therefore has to be incorporated into a bank of flowmeters of different sizes.
– Its uncalibrated uncertainty may not be adequate for some gas flow measurements.
– It will probably need to be calibrated.

The advantages are self evident, but the disadvantages need some further explanation. Because the flow through the nozzle can only change, assuming the temperature is constant, by varying the upstream pressure, the range of a nozzle is, in practice, rather limited. It is, therefore, customary to install a bank of nozzles of different throat sizes to allow a better range of flows. This is clearly less convenient than a flowmeter which has a wide range in one instrument. Its intrinsic accuracy may not be adequate for use as a source of calibration, so it may need to be calibrated for best performance.

APPLICATION
  – High precision gas flow measurement.
  – Transfer standard for gas flowmeter calibration.
COST – Medium to high.

The applications are those most appropriate to a research and development laboratory, or a manufacturer of small gas meters. However, some people advocate its wider use. Its initial cost will be fairly high due to the precision required in making a bank of nozzles.

4.5   OTHER DIFFERENTIAL PRESSURE DEVICES

Three types of device (all proprietary makes) where pressure is measured and which depend on differential pressure principles of varying sorts are illustrated in the box below. The Dall tube is similar to a nozzle or venturi, but has a recessed slot at the throat which should retain a vortex filament, and combines low head loss with high differential pressure compared with conventional devices. Other designs such as Lo-Loss also have a similarity to the nozzle and venturi and claim high precision such as ± 0.5 per cent of actual flow rate. Some designs are available for mounting between flanges, like an orifice plate.

The Gilflo-B has a spring loaded diaphragm causing a variable area orifice and resulting in a wide operating range (20:1 up to 100:1) for gas and steam, liquid natural gas, cryogenic, and other liquids.

Other variable area spring loaded meters have been used for measuring the flow rate of water, paraffin, petrol, oil, tar, distillates, etc. They can handle both high and low flows. The manufacturers claims for factory calibration are of the order of 1–2 per cent of maximum flow.

The viscous flowmeter for gases uses very small flow passages so that the

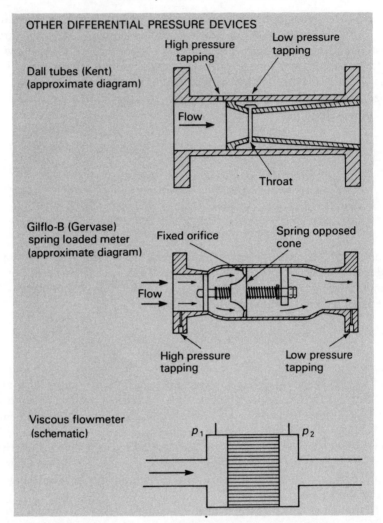

OTHER DIFFERENTIAL PRESSURE DEVICES

Dall tubes (Kent)
(approximate diagram)

High pressure tapping

Low pressure tapping

Flow

Throat

Gilflo-B (Gervase)
spring loaded meter
(approximate diagram)

Fixed orifice

Spring opposed cone

Flow

High pressure tapping

Low pressure tapping

Viscous flowmeter
(schematic)

p_1

p_2

pressure drop is due to the viscous as opposed to the inertia losses and thus is proportional to the flowrate. It was developed to measure gas flows in internal combustion engines where there is a high level of unsteadiness.

ADVANTAGES
In certain applications proprietary devices may offer the most satisfactory option.
DISADVANTAGES
Little independent operational information is available and it is necessary to rely on the manufacturers' values.

The advantages will be stressed by the manufacturer. The disadvantages are that little information is publicly available and the user is, therefore, dependent on the manufacturer for information on uncertainty, repeatability, range, maintenance, application, and so on. The potential user should ensure that data for a particular application is satisfactory.

Other differential devices exist, such as wedge meters, elbow meters, and swinging flap meters, and the reader will no doubt encounter even more. They either make use of the momentum, or the resulting displacement due to the passing fluid, or the measured pressure loss resulting from the flow.

The reader should refer to the manufacturer for advice on applications and initial cost, and if in doubt should seek expert advice.

4.6 TARGET METER (DRAG PLATE)

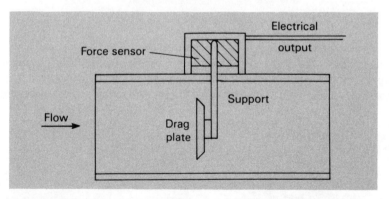

The drag plate is essentially an inside-out orifice plate. A plate is mounted in the pipe bore and this experiences a drag force around it. It is held against this force and the restraint exerted is used as a measure of the flowrate.

Thus, whereas the differential pressure across the orifice plate is measured, here the force on the plate which is linked to the pressure drop is measured. The advantage is that this can be done directly by an electrical method, such as a strain gauge.

For an incompressible fluid where the momentum change will only be due to redistribution of the velocity profile, the force on the plate will be approximately equal to the pressure drop times area, which is related to the momentum. The force is given by

$$F = C_D \tfrac{1}{2} \rho V^2 A \tag{4.7}$$

where C_D is the drag coefficient and A is the area of the target. This simple expression does not attempt to model the complex flow around the target meter, and implies a constancy of C_D which is likely to be only an approximation. It has been extended to two-phase flows, where it has been used with some success.

Because of the limited information on this flowmeter, it is important that information be obtained from the manufacturer on calibration, and so on.

PRECISION
If well constructed a random error less than 1% should be achievable.

INSTALLATION EFFECTS
It may be assumed that the effect of upstream installation is similar to that for the orifice and it is likely to be affected by pulsation.

These comments are reasonable assumptions based on the similarity of this meter to the orifice. Because of its similarity to the orifice it may be appropriate to assume similar installation requirements, although it is said to be less susceptible to upstream disturbances, particularly misalignment.

ADVANTAGES
Suitable for two-phase flow.
Electrical readout.

DISADVANTAGES
As for orifice.
Shortage of operational knowledge.

TYPICAL APPLICATIONS
As for orifice where standardization is not important. Two-phase flows.

PRICE – Medium.

It is perhaps an accident of history that the orifice is widely used and not the target meter, which is essentially an inside-out orifice plate meter. Had it been otherwise we might now have seen this instrument as part of a well-specified standard backed with much data, and offering the possibility of a direct electrical output.

Because it allows gas or solids entrained in the liquid to pass, the meter has been used for two-phase flows. It needs to be used with care and understanding in this application.

4.7 VARIABLE AREA, ROTAMETER, OR FLOAT-IN-TUBE

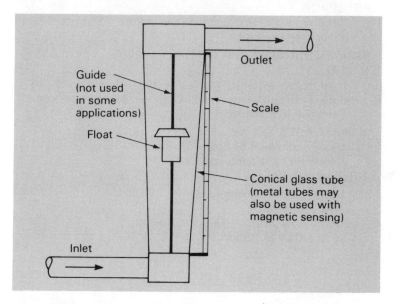

This is a vertical conical tube with the area increasing towards the top of the tube. Within the tube is a float which in some cases moves on an axial support. As the flow increases the drag on the float increases and causes it to rise in the tube. The rise of the float to a section of the tube with a greater cross-section reduces the drag due to the annular flow around the float. The float will thus settle at a height such that the upwards drag of the flow through the annulus around the float precisely balances the gravitational force on the float. Again the equations governing the movement of the float are essentially those for the orifice plate or target meter, except that the upward forces on the float are held constant and equal to the buoyant weight of the float, by the variation of the annulus area.

The indication is usually by viewing the height of the float on a calibrated scale on the glass tube. However, some designs use a metal tube and make use of a magnetic detector or other means of turning the float position into an electrical signal. Other designs use a restoring spring rather than gravity.

PRECISION
- Random error 0·2–2·0% upper range value (URV) depending on design.

RANGE TURNDOWN RATIO 10:1

INSTALLATION
- It must be installed vertically, but other effects are unlikely to cause appreciable change, except viscosity.
- Sensitive to pulsation.

ADVANTAGES
- Visual indication of flow rate.
- Simple to install and use.

DISADVANTAGES
- Density and viscosity sensitive.
- Low precision.
- Commonly without electrical readout.
- Affected by pulsation.

This is not a precision instrument and claims for high precision should be viewed with caution. It appears to be viscosity-dependent, and calibration may not be retained between different fluids. The flow enters around an inlet elbow, and so upstream conditions of flow are unlikely to have an undue effect on the response. The lift on the float is against gravity and so it is important that the tube be mounted vertically. If the flow is pulsatile the float may become very unstable. As for all momentum meters, it is density dependent.

A well-positioned variable area meter on a flow system may be seen from a distance and will provide a good indication of flow, and in this role it is most valuable. Unfortunately, many people use it as a precision instrument and do not question whether it is adequate for the application proposed.

TYPICAL APPLICATIONS
Liquid or gas flow indicator.
PRICE – Low.

4.8   MOMENTUM-SENSING FLOWMETERS – GENERAL COMMENTS

Differential pressure devices are often supposed to be of high accuracy and simple construction. This is not necessarily so. High accuracy (0·6 per cent uncertainty without calibration at best for the orifice, without allowing for pressure measurement errors) is only achieved with great care and precise manufacture. It is only maintained by regular inspection to ensure that the installation continues to meet the requirements of the standard.

Because they depend on the momentum change of the flow, which is proportional to the square of the velocity, there is a 'square-root' error introduced when the flow is unsteady or pulsatile. The inertia error is usually negligible in comparison with this one. However, the read-out device may also be sensitive to unsteady flows. Pressure tubes are notorious for introducing errors in the measurement of fluctuating pressures.

The situation with proprietary instruments is rather different. There is no publicly available mass of data to support the claims made for the instruments. It is, therefore, important that the manufacturer initially supplies evidence of performance so that the user may have confidence that the meter will come up to requirements. It is also important that the user knows how often the instrument should be inspected, overhauled, and recalibrated. This information must be sought from the manufacturer.

CHAPTER 5

Volumetric Flowmeters

5.1 POSITIVE DISPLACEMENT METERS

5.1 Positive displacement meters for liquids

The measured volume and stop watch still offer one of the most accurate methods of flow measurement, and this is essentially the principle of the positive displacement meter. The rotation of the meter allows well defined volumes of liquid or gas to pass through the meter. The volumes are contained either by means of sliding vanes which seal against the outer surface of the chamber, or by means of specially shaped rotors which keep contact as they rotate and cause a certain metered volume to be passed across the meter.

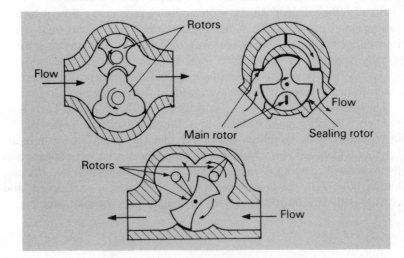

Three designs of *multi-rotor* meters are shown above. In these the rotors seal against each other. In some designs both rotors transmit fluid while in others one rotor transmits net fluid while the other provides a seal to return the rotor blades.

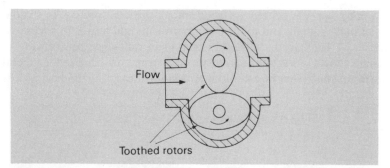

The *oval gear* meter is similar except that the seal between the rotors is enhanced by gear teeth on each rotor.

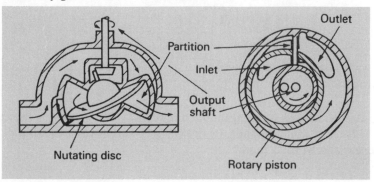

The *nutating disc* is constrained, by the central spherical bearing and by the transmission, to nutate. It is prevented from rotating by a partition which separates the inlet and outlet streams. The *rotary piston* is similar in that rotation is constrained by a partition causing a rocking motion which in turn causes the shaft, on which it is eccentrically mounted, to rotate.

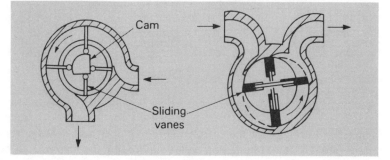

Sliding vane meters appear to be among the most precise. In these the vanes move radially out to form compartments and retract to release fluid and move back to the inlet side. The main difference between the two designs shown is that one operates on an internal cam while in the other the vanes are controlled by a contour within the measuring volume.

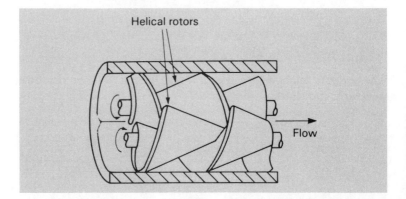

The *helical rotor* meter again traps liquid between the rotating members which are of complex shape. Its operation is hard to visualize without the benefit of a working model.

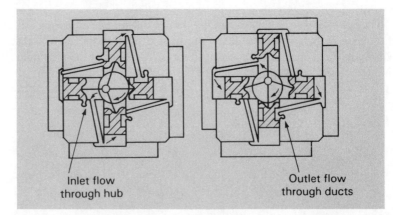

The *reciprocating piston* meter uses a system of open and closed ports to meter liquid via the volumes of each cylinder. In the example shown adjacent cylinders provide the valve operation by the position of the pistons.

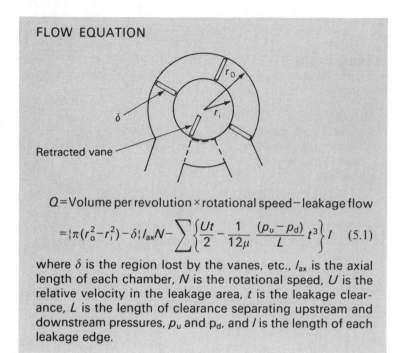

FLOW EQUATION

Q=Volume per revolution × rotational speed − leakage flow

$$=\{\pi(r_o^2-r_i^2)-\delta\}l_{ax}N-\sum\left\{\frac{Ut}{2}-\frac{1}{12\mu}\frac{(p_u-p_d)}{L}t^3\right\}l \quad (5.1)$$

where δ is the region lost by the vanes, etc., l_{ax} is the axial length of each chamber, N is the rotational speed, U is the relative velocity in the leakage area, t is the leakage clearance, L is the length of clearance separating upstream and downstream pressures, p_u and p_d, and l is the length of each leakage edge.

The geometry for a sliding vane meter serves to indicate the main features of a positive displacement (PD) meter's flow equation. The first term is straightforward, being the volume between inner and outer radii, less vane volume. The second term is derived from the leakage through a narrow parallel passage due to pressure drop and limited by μ, the viscosity

$$\frac{p_u-p_d}{L}=-\mu\frac{d^2u}{dy^2}$$

From this the flow through the leakage gap is obtained as

$$q=\left(\frac{1}{12\mu}\frac{p_u-p_d}{L}t^3+\frac{Ut}{2}\right)l$$

If the rotor is stationary and $U=0$, then it is clear that some leakage occurs and is a cause of concern where low rotational speeds cause it to represent a substantial fraction of the flow.

In practice, the meter is operated in a range such that the pressure dependent term is negligible and its size is checked by a 'slip' test, when the meter is turned very slowly to observe how much liquid escapes past the vanes.

Assuming that, ideally, the flow in the gap is carried with the vanes, we obtain the leakage in equation (5.1) above where the summation is for all leakage gaps.

PRECISION
Probable random error
 – Nutating disc of order ±0·5%.
 – oval gear of order ±0·1%.
 – sliding vane less than ±0·05%.

REPRODUCIBILITY
 – calibration should be checked within 6 months.

UNCERTAINTY
 – for high precision meters is limited by calibration rig uncertainty.

LINEARITY
 – of order ±0·05% (sliding vane).
 – other types probably better than ±0·5%.

RANGE TURNDOWN RATIO
 – claims from 10:1 to 20:1.
 – for water meters, 100:1 or greater.

INSTALLATION EFFECTS (High precision meters)
 – Upstream flow profile should have negligible effect.
 – Flows should be filtered to remove particles which may wear or block meter.
 – Gas bubbles will introduce errors.
 – Temperature compensation may be necessary.
 – Double case meters will be unaffected by pressure change.

As can be seen, precision of the meter is within very small tolerances, and with regular calibration the very high performance may be retained. However, this requires a regular schedule of calibration checks every six months, reducing to half the period if the uncertainty values are not retained.

Of all the common meters it is one of the few virtually unaffected by flow profile. However, it is a high precision instrument and not only must the fluid be particle free, but gas coming out of solution will severely affect readings, and temperature change will cause expansion of the chambers which, without compensation, may cause about 0·1 per cent change in 20°C. Liquid density change is at least ten times greater than this. Some meters are double skinned so that the measuring volume is unaffected by pressure differential. Where this is not the case 30 bar change will result in a change of the order of 0·1 per cent in the measuring volume. Changes in these parameters will also cause changes in leakage.

ADVANTAGES OF PRECISION INSTRUMENTS
  – Very high precision allowing use as a transfer standard.
  – Pulse output.

DISADVANTAGES
  – Bulky.
  – Can cause total line blockage.
  – Causes medium/high pressure loss.
  – May be damaged by sudden flow change.
  – Danger of corrosion if used for water.
  – May create flow pulsation.

The result of the design is a highly accurate meter which can be used to calibrate other devices, since it will retain its own calibration for long periods and during transport to other sites.

For the dispensing of hydrocarbon liquids the positive displacement meter has to operate over a wide flow range. Sudden start and stop of the flows would cause violent pressure waves which could damage the meter, and so the increase and decrease is achieved with a controlled acceleration and deceleration. At low flows the meter will tend to under-read.

The meter is large compared to other devices for the same capacity. It may also block the line if the vanes become jammed by particulate matter.

TYPICAL APPLICATIONS
  – Metering hydrocarbons (multi-rotor, sliding vane).
  – Calibration and transfer standard duties (sliding vane).
  – Oil hydraulics (oval gear).
  – Milk metering (rotary piston).
  – Water metering (rotary piston, nutating disc).

PRICE – High (for high precision instruments).
  – Low (for water meters)

It is particularly valuable for flows of high-value liquids where high precision and prior calibration are required. It is frequently used as a transfer standard and is installed in calibration rigs to provide a source of calibration for a flowmeter manufacturer. The rotary piston meter is used for hygienic applications. Cheaper designs are used for small flow lines of various liquids.

Existing commercial designs are unsuitable for slurries or multiphase flows.

The best of these devices are extremely high precision instruments and need to be treated and maintained with great care. When not in use they should be protected by a suitable inhibiting agent. They should not be subject to violent transients and pulsating flows should be avoided. At very low flows their performance is less good and 'slip' occurs, when more liquid passes than is registered. It is, therefore, important to restrict their operation at very low flows, and to test the extent of slip when checking the meter's calibration.

5.1.2 Positive displacement meters for gases
The roots blower is similar in concept to the twin rotor PD meters for liquids. The *wet gas meter* uses a water bath as the gas seal to create closed compartments for the transfer of the gas.

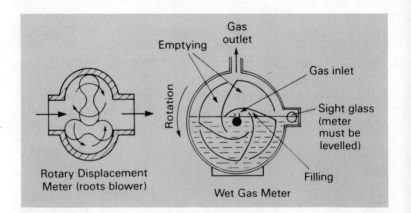

Rotary Displacement Meter (roots blower)

Wet Gas Meter

The diaphragm meter is essentially a piston meter in which compartments A, B, C, and D are the cylinders and the concertina provides a common piston for A and B and similarly for C and D.

PRECISION
Probable random error
- For Roots type meter; of the order of ±0·5%
- For wet gas meter; ±0·1%–0·25%
- For diaphragm meter; ±1%–3%

RANGE TURNDOWN RATIO
- For Roots type meter; 10:1 or higher.
- For wet gas meter; 10:1.
- For diaphragm meter; 50:1–150:1.

INSTALLATION EFFECTS
- Negligible effect from upstream conditions.
- Pulsation may affect performance.
- Diaphragm meter has restricted temperature range near ambient conditions.

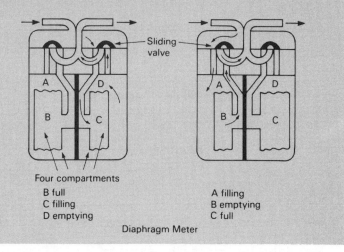

Sliding valve

Four compartments
B full
C filling
D emptying

A filling
B emptying
C full

Diaphragm Meter

The Roots type meter is capable of achieving the uncertainty values in the box above over a range of 10:1 or higher. The wet gas meter is a high precision meter capable of a similar operating range, but it tends to be rather bulky. The diaphragm meter is primarily used as a domestic gas meter and has a precision of about 2 per cent on a 50:1 range (or greater) to accommodate the range of domestic gas flows at one extreme for pilot flames and at the other extreme for boilers, etc. It retains its performance over long periods. It operates close to seasonal ambient conditions.

Another type of meter (the CVM meter) is very similar in concept to the multi-rotor liquid meter with a sealing rotor. It is claimed to be capable of better than 0·1 per cent precision. Most of these meters are primarily available with a mechanical output, rather than an electrical output.

To minimize pressure drop, a servo driven oval-gear meter is also available.

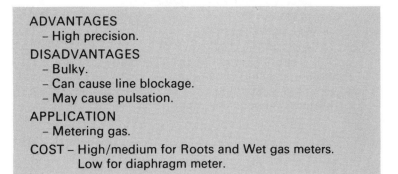

ADVANTAGES
  – High precision.
DISADVANTAGES
  – Bulky.
  – Can cause line blockage.
  – May cause pulsation.
APPLICATION
  – Metering gas.
COST – High/medium for Roots and Wet gas meters.
        Low for diaphragm meter.

5.2   TURBINE METERS

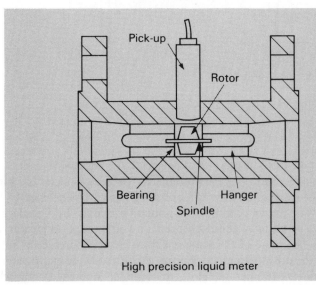

High precision liquid meter

The propeller and screw have a long and distinguished history in flow measurement. Provided the bearing drag is small and the blades are well designed, revolutions of the turbine wheel will give a good measure of the flow past the wheel. The revolutions may be measured by various means, but for the highest accuracy a low drag method is needed. Magnetic pickups are common, but optical fibres and also microwave techniques are used.

The liquid flowmeter ranges from instruments of very high precision, such as that shown above, to extremely robust low precision water meters,

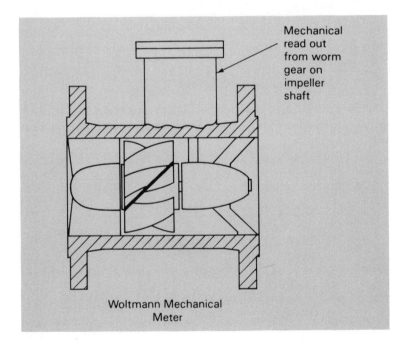

Mechanical read out from worm gear on impeller shaft

Woltmann Mechanical Meter

such as the Woltmann meter. Although the basic concept is the same, the application is very different.

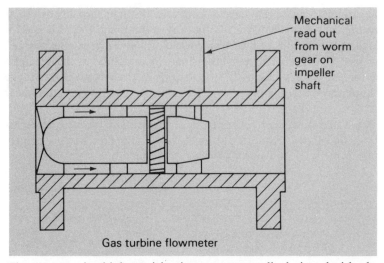

Gas turbine flowmeter

The gas meter is a high precision instrument usually designed with a large hub and small blades to create a high flow velocity and a high torque on the rotor.

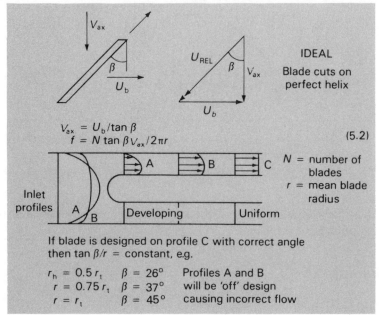

IDEAL

Blade cuts on perfect helix

$$V_{ax} = U_b/\tan \beta$$
$$f = N \tan \beta\, V_{ax}/2\pi r \qquad (5.2)$$

N = number of blades
r = mean blade radius

Inlet profiles

A
B
Developing   Uniform

If blade is designed on profile C with correct angle then $\tan \beta/r$ = constant, e.g.

$r_h = 0.5\, r_t$	$\beta = 26°$	Profiles A and B
$r = 0.75\, r_t$	$\beta = 37°$	will be 'off' design
$r = r_t$	$\beta = 45°$	causing incorrect flow

Many turbine meters use flat section blades. Ideally these will cut smoothly through the flow in a perfect helix. In the diagram above, V_{ax} = axial velocity, U_b = blade velocity, and U_{REL} = relative velocity of the fluid passing over the blade. Using this basic concept the value of V_{ax} can be obtained from the frequency of blade passing f. However, the theory is not, unfortunately, as simple as this, as the blades do not cut the fluid perfectly, and the value of β must change with radius to accommodate the profile across the pipe.

Suppose we consider the variation of blade angle for a uniform profile. It can be seen that, with no variation in axial velocity across the annulus, the blade angle changes from 26 to 45 degrees from hub to tip for a radius ratio of 1:2. If, however, profiles A and B existed, then flow will not meet the

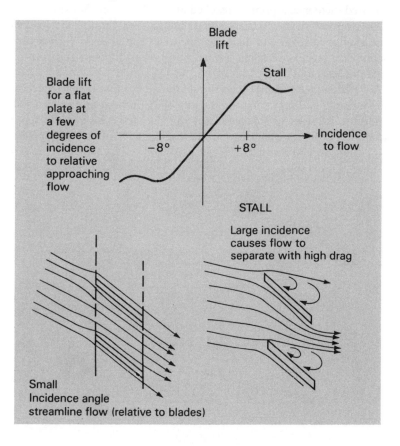

blades at the correct angle. It thus becomes apparent why the flowmeter will be susceptible to incorrect installation, since this will cause a flow profile which results in the wrong incidence angles at the blade for some parts of the annulus. It also suggests why a turbine wheel which is optimized for flow profile will give a better performance than one with constant angle blades.

An aerofoil at zero incidence causes an obstruction around which the flow accelerates. With increasing incidence the velocity on the top (or suction) surface increases with a consequent (see Bernoulli) drop in pressure.

On the lower (or pressure) surface the velocity is reduced and the pressure increases. Hence, a lift force is created across the aerofoil. With increased incidence a point is reached at which the aerofoil stalls.

The drag will be due to friction and pressure loss. For low incidences the drag change is small. As incidence increases the boundary layer on the suction side has to overcome an adverse pressure gradient and eventually separates, creating 'stall'.

A well designed turbine meter should operate so that the incidence at all radii is small, and at no time should any blade sections approach a stalled condition. In order to achieve this it will also be necessary to design the meter with bearings which minimize the drag, and with a sensing pick-up

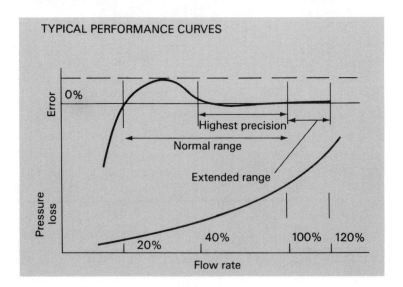

with negligible drag. Such a meter may then achieve a linear range of the order of 10:1, with high precision.

The drag is also influenced by the tip clearance between the ends of the blades and the turbine casing. A compromise must be achieved between too small a clearance, leading to a high drag, and too large a clearance, allowing some of the flow to pass the turbine without being 'metered'.

In practice the turbine meter closely approximates to a linear meter for high flow rates. The K factor, relates the flow rate to the frequency of pulses (and is also used for vortex meters). It is given by

$$K = \frac{\text{Pulses}}{\text{Unit volume}} \qquad (5.3)$$

The meter factor is usually defined as the ratio of the true volume passing through the meter to the indicated volume

$$\text{Meter factor} = \frac{\text{True volume}}{\text{Indicated volume}} \qquad (5.4)$$

However, other definitions are sometimes used, such as the reciprocal of the K factor.

At lower flowrates the drag becomes more significant until the flowmeter characteristic departs from a useful linear response. The meter can sometimes sustain a higher flowrate for short periods. However, there is a danger of over-speeding and damaging the bearings.

PRECISION
Probable random error
 – High precision liquid meters less than ±0·1%.
 – High precision gas meters less than ±0·5%.
 – Water meters less than ±1·0%.

REPRODUCIBILITY
 – calibration should be checked within 6 months (due to bearing wear).

UNCERTAINTY for high precision liquid turbine meters is probably limited by the uncertainty of the calibration rig.

LINEARITY
 – High precision liquid meters of order ±0·5%.
 – High precision gas meters of order ±1·0%.
 – Water meters ±2–5%.

RANGE TURNDOWN RATIO
  – High precision liquid meters 6:1 to 15:1.
  – Gas meters 10:1.
  – Water meters 50:1 or greater.
INSTALLATION EFFECTS
  – Sensitive to swirl since this will be relative rotation to the
    blades.
  – Sensitive to profile distortion due to blade stall and flow
    through tip gap.
  – Sensitive to viscosity.
  – Sensitive to particles in flow affecting bearings.
  – Sensitive to cavitation.
  – Gas turbine is sensitive to pulsating and varying flows.
  – For highest precision install a flow straightener 10 *D*
    upstream.

The turbine flowmeter can be calibrated to an accuracy better than
0·5 per cent over flow ranges of up to 10:1 and it, therefore, provides an
attractive method of fiscal monitoring, where frequent recalibration can be
built in to the system using, for instance, a pipe prover. It is also used as a
transfer standard, and in this application, it is best calibrated with upstream pipework and flow straightener to minimize the effects of upstream
disturbances. However, recalibration is necessary due to bearing wear in
particular. The water meter is a more robust, lower precision instrument of
much greater range.

With modern computer control and signal processing, the linearity
becomes less important as the calibration curve will be stored and flow
signals corrected from it.

The turbine meter is sensitive to swirl, particularly since swirl creates a
relative rotating environment, but the meter is also sensitive to other
upstream disturbances, and to viscosity.

The remarks above are primarily relevant to use with liquids, but they
are also partly true for gases, except that viscosity variation is less
important, density variation is more important, and upstream flow effects
appear to cause less error due in part to the large hub.

Solid particles may damage the flowmeter and steam may cause erosion.
Flowmeters for hygienic applications can also be damaged by over-
speeding when steam purging is used.

The gas turbine meter is affected by varying flows. The increasing flow creates higher incidence angles on the turbine blades and the turbine wheel accelerates fast. However, when the flow decreases the blades, presumably, stall with low lift and, hence, low deceleration. The effect is to give an over estimation of the total flow. The same occurs with pulsating flow, since, again, the turbine flowmeter cannot follow the fluctuating flow, and reads high.

BEARINGS

High precision liquid meters
- Ball bearings (process fluid lubrication):
  - Clean liquids.
    - Cryogenic liquids.
    - Petroleum liquids.
  - Self-balancing journal bearings:
  (material: tungsten carbide, PTFE, etc.).
    - Clean liquids.
      - Water.
      - Lubricating fluids.
  - Journal bearing with thrust ball:
    - Other liquids.
  - Bearingless:
    - Aggressive and non-lubricating liquids.

Gas meters.
  - Ball bearings with lubrication

The bearings are a critical part of the meter and must be of a suitable design and material for the application. Tungsten carbide is probably the most common bearing material, but titanium carbide, stellite, ceramics, etc., are also used. Bearing wear will affect the meter calibration.

Turbine meter bearings may be damaged if subject to fluctuating flows for extended periods. The bearings may also be designed for particular fluids, and may be damaged if used with other fluids. Special designs are available in which the rotor is 'bearingless' and usually has two blade rows which are supported by the flow.

The available data from turbine meters in two-phase flows suggests that they are subject to large errors. The reason for this is unclear, and so no operating guidelines can be suggested.

ADVANTAGES
 – Very high precision instruments used for fiscal measure-
   ments and custody transfer.
 – Linear over 6:1 range or more.
 – Robust mechanical water meters are also available.

DISADVANTAGES
 – Use with upstream straightener and filter for best results.
 – Affected by viscosity (avoid use with liquids of viscosity
   above 25cSt for highest performance).
 – Recalibrate regularly due to bearing wear.
 – Can be damaged by over-speeding.
 – Gas flowmeter over-reads in pulsating flow.

TYPICAL APPLICATIONS
Single phase liquids and gases without excessive flows,
either high or low, particularly where high precision is
required. Usually electrical frequency output; water metering where mechanical readout is required. (For very low
flows use a pelton wheel type.)

PRICE
 – Medium.
 – Low for water meters.

The flowmeter is widely used to monitor liquid hydrocarbon flows in
North Sea oil pipelines, and is usually installed with a prover to allow
regular recalibration. In high precision instruments two pick-ups are
common to provide a check value. The flowmeter needs careful installation
and maintenance. In one gas installation with a varying flow of about
100 seconds period the author estimated an over-reading of a few per cent.

Designs using a blade row which is like a pelton wheel allow very low
flows to be measured.

Several designs position the turbine or propeller in a by-pass line across
an obstruction such as an orifice plate. The flow in the main line will then be
proportional to the flow in the by-pass, but the meter will need to be
calibrated.

Some recent designs of turbine flowmeters have two rotors. The one
illustrated below has a slave rotor, the object of which is to drive the main
shaft, and thus reduce the bearing drag of the main indicating turbine rotor
to a very low level. The pick-up drag is reduced to a negligible value by

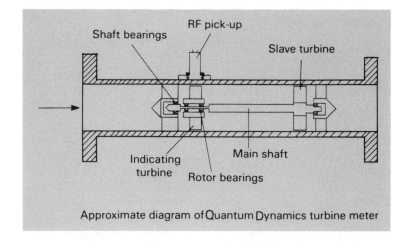

Approximate diagram of Quantum Dynamics turbine meter

using a radio frequency signal. The result is a turbine meter which is claimed to have a very high precision over a very wide range.

Another design is very similar to the gas turbine illustrated above, but with a second rotor in close proximity which senses the rotation of the flow leaving the main rotor, and uses this to check that installation, performance, and so on, have not changed from calibration and initial installation.

Price will vary according to quality and size. However, the water meters are very low price.

5.3 OSCILLATORY METERS

The most important of the oscillating fluid meters is the vortex meter, and this will be discussed at length. At the end of this section we will briefly discuss the fluidic flowmeter. A third device, the Swirl meter, will not be discussed in detail. It depends on the creation of a strong vortex with a set of blades. The vortex is swept downstream into a pipe contraction. The effect of this is to cause the vortex to rotate within the pipe at a speed proportional to the flowrate. The rotation is then sensed and related to flowrate. This device is used for gas and liquid flow measurements and has a turndown ratio of 10:1–30:1.

The vortex flowmeter consists of a bluff body within a circular pipe. The width of the body is about 25–30 per cent of the pipe diameter, and the familiar vortex shedding behind a cylinder is greatly stabilized by the short

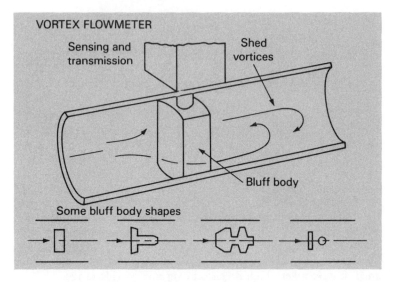

body with, effectively, end plates formed by the pipe wall. Also the body has very well defined edges from which the vorticity is shed, unlike the circular cylinder.

The most common body shapes approximate to a rectangle or a triangle. Sensors depend on various physical parameters, and some will be more suited to particular fluids. Some sensors are mounted in a second body downstream of the shedding body. The instrument appears to have a similar characteristic for liquids and gases.

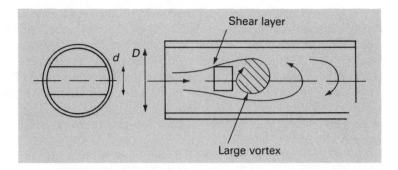

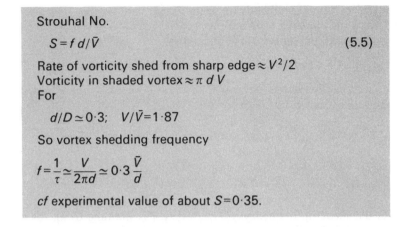

The box above gives the formula for S, the Strouhal number, based on $\bar{V}$, the mean velocity of the pipe.

The box also gives an order-of-magnitude model for the value of the shedding frequency. Vorticity, the spin imparted to a fluid by shear, is shed from the sharp edge of the bluff body into the large rolling-up vortex until it is 'full' and is then shed downstream. The time to 'fill' this large vortex is inversely proportional to the frequency, f.

This is only an approximate indication of how the shedding comes about. However, it is interesting to note the closeness of the result to the experimental value. It is first assumed that the vorticity has a value of V/δ, where δ is the thickness of the boundary layer. The rate of shedding will be approximately the rate at which a layer of thickness δ and mean velocity $V/2$ leaves the corner of the bluff body.

Thus, we can calculate the rate of vorticity shedding as

Vorticity × Shedding rate

$$\frac{V}{\delta} \times \frac{\delta V}{2} = \frac{V^2}{2}$$

The vorticity in the roll vortex will be equal to the circulation around it, and this is given by the product

Circumference × Velocity

$$= \pi d \times V$$

A typical ratio of bluff body thickness to pipe diameter (0·3) is assumed, and from this the area ratio and, hence, the velocity ratio past the body compared with the pipe area is obtained as

$$V_{ax} = \bar{V}/(1 - 4d/\pi D)$$

The actual velocity leaves the body at an angle. If we guess the angle as, say, 30 degrees we can write

$$V \approx V_{ax}/\cos 30°$$

or

$$\frac{V}{\bar{V}} \simeq 1·87$$

Thus the shedding frequency, $f = 1/\tau$, where τ is the time to fill the roll vortex and $f = 0·3\ \bar{V}/d$.

SENSORS	COMMENTS
Thermistor	either in upstream facing or in transverse flow duct.
Pressure	sensed by diaphragm or by moving tail.
Shuttle ball	movement sensed magnetically.
Strain gauge	on deflector beam.
Ultrasonic	modulated by vortices.
Other proposals	hot wire; optical fibre.

The method of sensing the vortices varies according to manufacturer and application. The most common currently available depend on pressure sensing, either using diaphragms giving an electrical readout due to capacitance, or using strain gauges, or using a deflecting tail. Because of the wide range possible, the pressure fluctuations may have a range of 100:1 or more, and the change from liquid to gas will extend this. It must, therefore, be the objective of manufacturers to produce a design which, with a single sensor, covers this range. Ultrasonics may offer this possibility.

The K factor (pulses/unit volume) is a measure of performance used for this type of meter also (*cf* equations (5.3) (5.4)).

PRECISION
- probable random error less than ±0·5%.

LINEARITY
- probably better than ±1·0%.

RANGE TURNDOWN RATIO
- 10:1 or greater.
- minimum Re about 10 000

INSTALLATION EFFECTS
- In general allow at least as much as for an orifice plate.
- Avoid protuberances upstream due to gaskets, weld beads, etc., and pipe diameter changes.

Claims for precision are varied, and the value suggested will be disputed as both too high and too low. Claims have been made for very large operating ranges, but 15:1 is probably achievable, and may be exceeded in some designs.

The meter appears to be very sensitive to upstream disturbance, presumably because any fitting upstream will change the vorticity within the flow and this will affect the vortex shedding. Some manufacturers even emphasize the importance of a smooth pipe upstream, free of protuberances and diameter changes. Great care should be taken if the calibration of the meter is to be retained.

The range of operation of these meters is limited by the strength and stability of shedding for low Reynolds numbers. A minimum value for Re in the range 10 000–30 000 is usual. There may be problems with compressibility for gases and cavitation for liquids at the upper end of the range. Their size range is also limited since, as the size of the bluff body increases, so the shedding frequency falls until it is too low to obtain a reasonable response.

ADVANTAGES
- Linear frequency output.
- Low sensitivity to temperature and viscosity.
- Suitable for liquid and gas.

DISADVANTAGES
- Good installation essential.
- Not suitable for multiphase flow.
- Cavitation and compressibility errors at extreme flows.
- Flow pulsation may cause errors.

This meter is comparable with the orifice plate meter. It has an area ratio equivalent to a $\beta \simeq 0.8$ and a pressure drop of similar amount. It lacks the mass of data which the orifice plate has acquired through many years of testing, but it has the great advantages of linearity, electrical frequency output, and wider range. The range, although limited by vortex shedding stability, is several times greater than that for the orifice. It appears to be relatively insensitive to fluid properties and some tests have indicated calibrations on gas and liquid to be virtually the same.

The flowmeter is very sensitive to upstream flow distortion and very careful installation is recommended by the manufacturers. It is also sensitive to spurious frequencies due to flow pulsation. A second phase, although it may leave the vortex shedding unaffected, may upset the sensing element.

TYPICAL APPLICATIONS
  – Liquid flows and gas flows in pipes of 18–200 mm, e.g., water, milk, hydrocarbons, air, and other gases.
PRICE – Medium.

Applications are similar to those for orifice plates and in a similar way will be limited by experience, except that each design of vortex meter will have a different sensitivity to particular liquids and gases, and no general rules will be usable.

The device has begun to find a niche in some of the applications where an orifice plate would have been used. However, its sensing systems have not proved as straightforward as may have been expected.

Another oscillating device which is creating increasing interest is the fluidic flowmeter.

The jet from the inlet duct oscillates between Channel A and B due to feedback via Channel A′ and B′. Its frequency of oscillation is proportional to the volumetric flow rate. It has attracted interest due to its potentially very large operating range, low flow capability, and linearity.

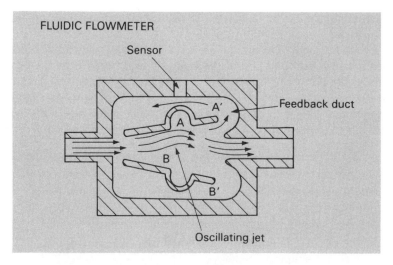

FLUIDIC FLOWMETER

Sensor

Feedback duct

A'

A

B

B'

Oscillating jet

5.4   ELECTROMAGNETIC FLOWMETERS

When a fluid flows through a non-magnetic tube in a transverse magnetic field, voltages and currents are generated in the fluid due to the motion. (The inner surface of the tube is covered with an insulating liner to avoid shorting out the small voltages.) If the voltage is measured between two electrodes in the pipe wall it will provide an indication of the volumetric flowrate in the pipe. The correct design of the pipe and magnetic coils is

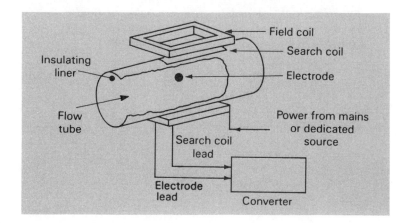

Field coil

Search coil

Insulating liner

Electrode

Flow tube

Power from mains or dedicated source

Search coil lead

Electrode lead

Converter

essential to achieve a flowmeter which is little affected by upstream disturbance.

Two main types of excitation are used. For many years all flowmeters used a sinusoidal excitation of the magnetic field supplied by the mains. This results in a 'transformer' type spurious voltage being generated and the electrode wires, amplifier, and so on, had to be designed to eliminate this voltage. This voltage and the eddy currents in the pipe walls led in particular to 'zero drift' – the variation of the output at no-flow by 1 per

The voltage generated across the flowmeter between the electrodes satisfies the equation

$$\Delta U = SBD\bar{V} \tag{5.6}$$

where

    S is the sensitivity
    B is a representative value of the magnetic flux density
    D is the pipe diameter
    $\bar{V}$ is the mean velocity in the pipe

If

    (a) the magnetic field is uniform
    (b) flow profile is axisymmetric

Then $S = 1$

If a flowmeter is subject to an arbitrary rectilinear flow, then a weight function may be calculated which indicates the importance of flow in each part of the pipe cross section.

Shercliff weight function for uniform magnetic field
The velocity at any point in the cross section 'weights' the signal by the amount shown (for one quadrant).

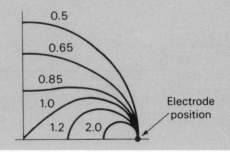

cent or so of the full scale reading. In modern designs this has been largely eliminated and, in addition, many designs have a low-flow cut-off, whereby the signal is set to zero below a certain flow rate.

As a result of these problems, square wave excitation was introduced. The actual square wave pattern is different for different manufacturers, but, essentially, a sufficient dwell period at two different field excitation levels allows spurious voltages to decay and the flow signal to be obtained as a difference between the two levels.

The last comment covers an extensive design method which has allowed progress from the simple flowmeter with a uniform field (for which one quadrant of the weight function is shown) which was bulky and could not always be suitably installed, to compact flowmeters with low susceptibility to profile effects. Modern designs are unlikely to have a uniform magnetic field; S is unlikely to be unity, and the weight function, if available, will indicate likely performance in disturbed flows. The guidelines below are a simple distillation of the available data.

PRECISION
Random error probably less than ±0·5%.

LINEARITY
– probably better than ±0·5%.

RANGE TURNDOWN RATIO
– 10:1 or 100:1 on multiple ranges.

Installation Guidelines
– The error due to a reducer installed next to the flowmeter is likely to be less than 1%.
– An error of up to 2% should be assumed for other fittings separated from the meter (electrode plane) by 5 D of straight pipe.
– An error of 1% may occur for other fittings separated from the meter by 10 D of straight pipe.
– The orientation of the flowmeter at 5 D spacing or greater does not simply correlate with the size of the error.
– A pipe fitting at least 2 D downstream of the electrode plane should not affect the response.

The precision is typical of most electromagnetic flowmeters currently available. The effect of upstream pipe fittings is less than for most other types of flowmeter. The flowmeter should be installed with at least 10 *D* upstream between fitting and electrode plane to avoid additional uncertainty in excess of 1 per cent. Although theoretical considerations indicate that flowmeter orientation is important, in practice the developing flow from a fitting is so complex that the orientation should be decided on other grounds, notably that the electrodes are kept in a horizontal plane. Downstream pipe work should have negligible effect, and two diameters should be ample.

Among the many recent designs, two trends are of particular importance. The wafer design for fitting between flanges has a much shorter axial length than more conventional meters. It may be affected by the magnetic and conducting properties of the neighbouring pipework. The non-contacting electrode designs offer the possibility of electrode shapes such that the meter is almost insensitive to profile. This insensitivity may also be achieved with a square section pipe bore.

It is important to obtain advice on material compatibility with the operating liquid both for the liner and the electrodes. Typical liner materials are neoprene, polyurethane, PTFE, and ceramic, and typical electrode materials are non-magnetic stainless steel, platinum–iridium, tantalum, hastelloy, etc. Most manufacturers offer an electrode cleaning system, which is an important additional feature to retain performance.

ADVANTAGES
- Linear response.
- Clear bore.
- Signal down to zero flow (if required).
- Low sensitivity to upstream conditions.
- No moving parts.
- Suitable for slurries and multiphase flows.

DISADVANTAGES
- Only suitable for conducting liquids (commercially) (or in multiphase the continuous phase should be conducting).

The advantages need little comment. The signal is usable down to zero flow. Early versions exhibited a drift of ± 1 per cent or more which, at zero flow, caused concern. However, virtually no other meter can continue to read with any reliability to such low values. It has created a particular niche in slurry flow measurement. Indeed, an early application was for flow measurement in dredging operations. It measures the volume flow rate, assuming that this has the velocity of the conducting phase and fills the whole cross section.

Although it has been made to operate on non-conducting liquids, it is available commercially for liquids with conductivity greater than about 5 μS/cm or, for non-contacting electrodes, about 0·05 μS/cm. Tap water has conductivity of about 100 μS/cm. The actual conductivity is not important, provided it is adequate, uniform, and the electrodes are not 'open-circuited' by air or fouling.

> **APPLICATIONS**
>   – Water, slurry, conducting chemicals, liquid foods, drinks, sewage, liquid metals, etc.
> **COST** – Medium.

The list of applications is very long. It should be considered for any conductive liquid where flow measurement is required. There can be problems where the tube runs partially empty and/or where the electrodes lose contact with the fluid. Bubbles may interfere with the continuity. The price may be higher than for some other types of flowmeter, but for many applications this instrument offers an obstruction-free, reliable, electrical-output meter of good precision and needing low maintenance. In smaller sizes they tend to be more expensive than their competitors, and in very large sizes can be very expensive.

5.5 ULTRASONIC METERS

These fall into three categories or modes of operation and, while some commercial designs combine two operating modes in one instrument, it is simpler to deal with each independently.

5.5.1 Transit time ultrasonic meter

The time-of-flight designs are precision instruments. The difference in the time of transit between transducers of upstream and downstream pulses of ultrasound is used to obtain the flowrate in the tube. However, the signal is dependent on the speed of sound. The transit time (or leading edge)

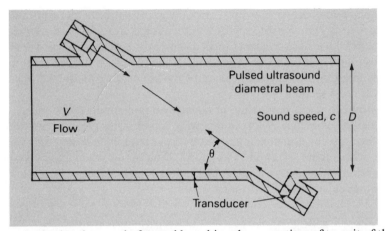

system obtains the speed of sound by taking the mean time of transit of the pulses up and downstream.

The sing-around system eliminates the value of c by obtaining the sing-around frequencies resulting from pulse trains across the pipe created by the received pulse triggering a transmitted pulse. Thus, as one pulse is received at one transducer it triggers a pulse from the other transducer. The upstream and the downstream pulse trains each have their own frequency, and the difference between the frequencies allows the flowrate to be obtained. In most designs the same pair of transducers operate in both directions.

TRANSIT TIME

Time of upstream pulse

$$t_u = \frac{D/\sin\theta}{c - V\cos\theta}$$

Time of downstream pulse

$$t_d = \frac{D/\sin\theta}{c + V\cos\theta}$$

$$\left.\begin{array}{l} \Delta t = t_u - t_d = 2\,VD\cot\theta/c^2 \\ t_m = (t_u + t_d)/2 = D\mathrm{cosec}\theta/c \end{array}\right\} \qquad V = \frac{D\,\Delta t}{t_m^2\,\sin 2\theta} \qquad (5.7)$$

SING-AROUND

Upstream frequency

$$f_u = \frac{c - V\cos\theta}{D/\sin\theta};$$

Downstream frequency

$$f_d = \frac{c + V\cos\theta}{D/\sin\theta}$$

$$\Delta f = f_d - f_u = V\sin 2\theta/D \qquad\qquad (5.8)$$

Transit time

Dia. (mm)	$(t_u + t_d)/2$ (s)	Δt (s)	$E(\Delta t)$ (s)
100	10^{-4}	10^{-7}	10^{-9}
300	3×10^{-4}	3×10^{-7}	3×10^{-5}

($\theta = 45$ degrees, $V = 1$ m/s, and c is taken as 1430 m/s, the value for water at 4°C.)
($E(\Delta t)$ is discrimination in Δt required to achieve an uncertainty of better than 1%.)

Two ultrasound pulses are transmitted, one upstream and one down stream. The upstream pulse is retarded by the flow and takes longer to reach the receiving transducer, while the downstream pulse is speeded up and takes a shorter time. From these two values of elapsed time the speed of sound (mean) and the flowrate (difference) obtained. It is important to obtain the sound speed, as the accuracy is directly dependent on it, and the sound speed is affected by temperature, fluid parameters, etc. Precision of the instrument will depend on the smallest time which can be measured. To obtain 1 per cent uncertainty time must be measured for a 100 mm tube to within one nanosecond.

Sing-around

	$V = 1$ m/s		$V = 10$ m/s	
Dia.	f_d Hz	Δf Hz	f_d Hz	Δf Hz
100	10117	10	10162	100
300	3372	3·3	3387	33

($\theta = 45$ degrees and c is taken as 1430 m/s, the value for water at 4°C.)

The limitation for the sing-around system relates more to the very low frequencies and long time periods needed to achieve sufficient accuracy. To achieve 1 per cent uncertainty we shall need to have a measuring period of greater than 1 s for the most favourable of these cases.

INTEGRAL FOR NON-UNIFORM PROFILE

$$\Delta t = \frac{2\cot\theta}{c^2} \int V(x)\, dx$$ (5.9)

Integration is along a diameter
in the plane of the beam

$$\Delta f = \frac{\sin 2\theta}{D^2} \int V(x)\, dx$$ (5.10)

A further problem results from the line integral inherent in ultrasonic flowmeter systems. For a single beam flowmeter with the path across the diameter of the tube, simple integration of the fully developed turbulent profiles for various Reynolds numbers shows that, for each 10:1 turndown, the diametral integration introduces an error of about ± 0.5 per cent. In addition, single beam designs are very susceptible to distortions in the flow profile due to upstream fittings. For this reason multiple beams are used to improve accuracy by integrating across several pipe chords. Two-beam designs have an almost correct integration for fully developed profiles, and they also give a much improved performance in distorted profiles. Instruments with more than two beams are very high precision specialist instruments and can achieve high performance based on measurement of path length, angle, etc., without calibration.

The ultrasound is transmitted and received by piezo-electric crystals (in most designs) which are incorporated into the transducer to achieve certain characteristics such as damping, directionality etc. Various designs of transducer are available including retro-fit (hot tap) and clamp-on transducers which can be used on existing pipework. The latter designs allow the instrument to be installed on the outside of a pipe without breaking into the pipe. It is usually necessary to specify the dimensions and material of the pipe when ordering such an instrument.

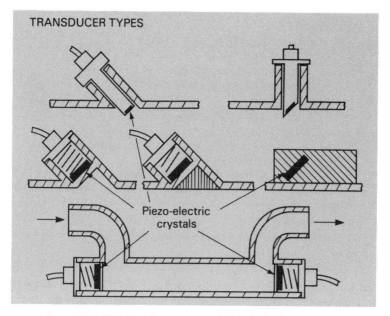

TRANSDUCER TYPES

Piezo-electric
crystals

For small pipes the flow is brought into the pipe from the side and flows axially between the transducers. The advantage of this is that a greater length can be used resulting in a greater time difference for up- and downstream pulses than would occur by traversing only a small pipe diameter.

PRECISION
- probable random error for liquids and gases less than ±1%.

LINEARITY
- probably better than ±1%.

RANGE TURNDOWN RATIO
- for liquids 10:1 to 20:1 or higher.
- for gases 50:1 or higher.

INSTALLATION
- 1 beam; very sensitive to upstream flow distortion.
- 2 beam; allow at least 10 D straight pipe between flowmeter and upstream pipe fittings.

ADVANTAGES
- No obstruction to flow.
- Capability of retrofitting
- Available in clamp-on designs.
- Probably unaffected by pulsatile flow.
- Suitable for most single phase liquids.
- Suitable for high pressure gas flows.

DISADVANTAGES
- Transducer cavities may collect air or debris.
- Response time may be slow.
- Unsuitable for most two-phase flows.
- Piezo-electric crystals must be in contact with gas in most designs.

APPLICATIONS
- Water, oil, and high pressure gas flows, etc.

COST – Medium/high.

The value of precision is possibly pessimistic, but there is a wide range of instrument performance. The errors due to installation downstream of a pipe fitting on a single beam meter can be high, and manufacturers should be consulted on the required upstream straight lengths to retain performance. These may be as great as for an orifice plate. The two beam meter is much superior, and the value of $10D$ given should be adequate for most upstream disturbances purposes. One recent design has been specifically developed for measuring the flow of mud, an unusual application for an ultrasonic transit-time meter. The cost bracket will depend on both the quality of the instrument and also on the number of paths. The two beam instruments tend to be rather more expensive than the single beam, but this may be worthwhile to obtain the better performance. Instruments with more than two beams are usually very expensive.

5.5.2 Ultrasonic correlation flowmeter

Two-diametral acoustic paths displaced in the axial direction allow two received signals, disturbed by the turbulence or a second phase in the flow, to be correlated, and the time lag in the downstream signal to be obtained as a measure of the transit time of the fluid between paths.

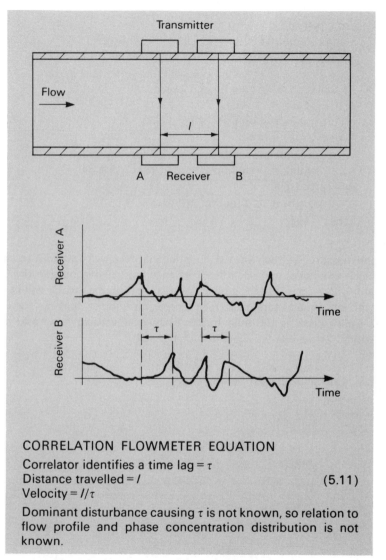

CORRELATION FLOWMETER EQUATION

Correlator identifies a time lag = τ
Distance travelled = l (5.11)
Velocity = l/τ

Dominant disturbance causing τ is not known, so relation to flow profile and phase concentration distribution is not known.

Equation (5.11) depends on the correlation time for a travelling disturbance over distance l. However, because of the uncertainty relating to the position of the disturbance, it is not clear precisely what flow rate is

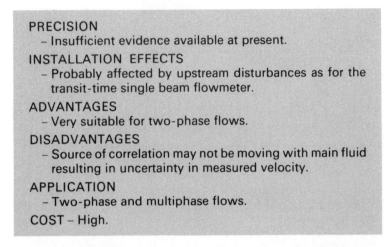

PRECISION
  – Insufficient evidence available at present.
INSTALLATION EFFECTS
  – Probably affected by upstream disturbances as for the transit-time single beam flowmeter.
ADVANTAGES
  – Very suitable for two-phase flows.
DISADVANTAGES
  – Source of correlation may not be moving with main fluid resulting in uncertainty in measured velocity.
APPLICATION
  – Two-phase and multiphase flows.
COST – High.

being measured by such a device. Commercial design(s) have only recently become available, and so little experience is available outside the laboratory. It is clear that the greater the disturbance, the greater will be the signal, but some disturbances, for example, air bubbles, may not travel at the same speed as the fluid (particularly in a vertical flow) and may eventually attenuate the signal too much.

5.5.3 Ultrasonic doppler flow monitor

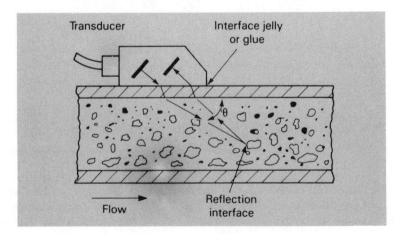

If acoustic waves reflect off a moving object and return to the source it is found that they experience a frequency shift proportional to the velocity component of the object parallel to the acoustic beam. This shift can be used to obtain the velocity of particles or discontinuities in a flowing fluid.

DOPPLER FLOWMETER EQUATION

Transmitted frequency = f_t.

Frequency shift of reflected signal

$$= \Delta f = 2 f_t (V/c) \cos\theta \qquad\qquad (5.12)$$

It is not known from which moving interface the reflection comes and, hence, how V relates to the mean fluid velocity.

Equation (5.12) for the doppler frequency shift incorporates the speed of sound. This will vary, and some form of compensation should be incorporated. However, the major uncertainty relates to the nature of the reflecting surface. It appears to be necessary for the flow to be multiphase, even if the second phase component is very small, although temperature fluctuations may provide sufficient reflection in some cases. There is always an uncertainty as to the relative velocity of the reflecting particles, etc., and their position within the pipe. This is particularly severe in a vertical flow. The device has, therefore, to be viewed as a flow indicator, and, in that role, can be very useful.

Several devices of this type are available and they offer one of the few methods of determining whether or not flow is occurring in a pipe without needing to disturb the pipework. However, they have definite limitations which must be understood.

If used intelligently they can provide the engineer with a very valuable diagnostic tool.

PRECISION – low.

ADVANTAGES
- Easily installed without disturbing pipe work.

DISADVANTAGES
- Requires a second phase even if in small quantities and dispersed, or fluid variation.
- Reflecting interface may not have velocity of bulk flow – particularly in vertical flows.
- Vibrations may cause spurious readings.

APPLICATIONS
- Where a simple flow monitor can be used as an additional indicator.

COST – low.

CHAPTER 6

Mass Flowmeters

6.1 INTRODUCTION

(1) True Mass Flow Measurement
   – Sensor responds to mass flow.
(2) Inferential Mass Flow Measurement
   – Separate sensors respond to velocity or momentum
     and pressure, temperature, etc.
NOTES
   – The categorization is somewhat misleading as single
     sensors are subject to other effects, while dual sensors
     may give a true measure.
   – For fluids with known properties inferential methods
     may be used.
   – For fluids with unknown properties true mass flow
     measurement, or flow and density will be required.

Mass flow measurement has become categorized as 'true mass flow measurement' and 'inferential mass flow measurement'. This categorization is somewhat misleading, as a single sensor is subject to other effects, while dual sensors may give a true measure of mass flow. Certain meters using heat capacity are sometimes referred to as true mass flowmeters, since heat capacity is mass specific. But heat capacity is dependent on the fluid and, therefore, the meter will only read correctly if the fluid properties are known. In addition, the heat transfer is viscosity dependent. In contrast, a combination of a volumetric flowmeter and a density meter may be less dependent on fluid properties.

An alternative categorization might be in terms of meters for fluids of 'known' and 'unknown' properties. For the latter, a mass meter would need to be sensitive only to mass flow and unaffected by fluid change, second or third phases, unsteadiness, and so on. It is unlikely that any meter is totally unaffected at present. Therefore, we will review briefly the various types on their merits.

A combination of a volumetric meter of well-documented performance and insensitive to fluid properties with a density meter of the vibrating tube type, or some other well tried design, allows mass flow to be deduced. However, the two readings may not refer to the same piece of fluid which in some applications could be a disadvantage.

EXAMPLES OF MASS FLOW MEASUREMENT WITH FLUIDS OF KNOWN PROPERTIES

Differential Pressure Meter

$$q_m = CE\varepsilon \frac{\pi}{4} d^2 \sqrt{(2\rho_1 \Delta p)} \qquad (4.1)$$

Required measurements Δp; and ρ or p and T, etc.

Ultrasonic flowmeter
 - Liquid

$$q_m = \frac{\pi D \, \Delta t}{8 \, k_s \cot\theta} \qquad (6.1)$$

 - Gas

$$q_m = \frac{\pi D \, \gamma p \, \Delta t}{8 \cot\theta} \qquad (6.2)$$

Required measurements Δt; and for liquid k_s=adiabatic compressibility – and is little affected by p, but more so by T; for gases, p and a value of γ.

Flowmeters may offer the possibility of conversion from normal use to mass flow by obtaining additional information from existing measurements. The differential pressure devices require a value for ρ, the density, for both volumetric and mass measurement. This may be obtained by use of a density cell of some sort, or by measuring p, the pressure, and T, the temperature, for a gas and deducing ρ, knowing the gas law for that particular gas. With Δp this then provides a value for q_m the mass flowrate.

The ultrasonic flowmeter includes c^2, the square of the sound speed, in its equation. We may rearrange the equation to replace c^2 by expressions which include density. These are given below for liquids and gases:

for liquids, $c^2 = \dfrac{1}{k_s \rho}$

for gases, $c^2 = \dfrac{\gamma p}{\rho}$

and by combining ρ with q_v, where k_s is the adiabatic compressibility, and γ is the ratio of the specific heats, we obtain q_m. We need to measure or know k_s for liquids and γ and p for gases. In addition, an acoustic impedance measurement may provide a value for ρc. Values of γ for some gases are as tabulated below.

Gas	γ		Gas	γ
A	1·67	Monatomic	CO_2	1·31
He	1·67		CH_4	1·31
Air	1·40		C_2H_6	1·19
N_2	1·40		CH_6	1·15
O_2	1·40	Diatomic		
H_2	1·41			
CO	1·40			

Many other types of volumetric meter may also be used in combination with a density measurement.

MULTIPLE SENSORS

ADVANTAGES
- Volumetric flow known precisely.
- Density may be deduced from existing measurements or measured with a density cell.
- Mass flow may be programmed using modern techniques.

DISADVANTAGES
- Two measurements required, which may not correspond to the same piece of fluid.

6.2 THERMAL MASS FLOW MEASUREMENT

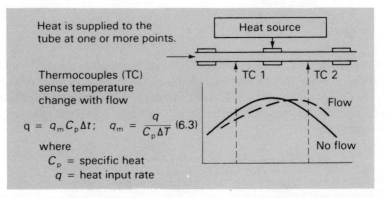

Heat is supplied to the tube at one or more points.

Heat source

Thermocouples (TC) sense temperature change with flow

TC 1   TC 2

Flow

No flow

$$q = q_m C_p \Delta t; \quad q_m = \frac{q}{C_p \Delta T} \quad (6.3)$$

where

C_p = specific heat
q = heat input rate

Heat is supplied to the gas passing through a tube so that the temperature rises. This rise is proportional to the mass flow rate for a particular fluid and is measured by, for example, two thermocouples. The temperature rise, assuming that all this heat is transferred, is also proportional to the heat capacity of the fluid, which must be known. The specific heat for some gases (specific heat at constant pressure) is given in the table below.

Gas	C_p (KJ/kgK)	Variation (% per °C)	Variation with pressure (%)	
			0–10 bar	0–100 bar
Air	1·01	0·01	2	16
N_2	1·04	0·012	0·1	1·6
O_2	0·92	0·02	1	18
CO_2	0·83	0·004	10	—
CH_4	2·33	0·11	2	31

This table indicates that the flowmeter must be calibrated on the correct gas and operating pressure.

The device is also likely to be affected by heat transfer rate, and this will be affected, in turn, by the nature of the fluid plus the condition of the pipe. If the device operates in the laminar flow regime, then turbulence effects will not be present.

It is sometimes claimed to be a true mass flowmeter, but is too much affected by other parameters for this to be an adequate description.

For larger flows the sensor is mounted in a bypass with a laminar flow element in the main pipe to ensure that the flowrate in the bypass is proportional to that in the main. The device is typically of small size (3–6 mm tube) and for low flows.

PRECISION
 – Random error probably less than 0·5% Upper Range Value (URV).

RANGE TURNDOWN RATIO
 – 20:1–50:1.

INSTALLATION
 – Unlikely to be affected by flow profile.

ADVANTAGES
 – Capable of measuring very low gas mass flows and liquid flows.

DISADVANTAGES
 – Preferably calibrated on the correct gas at close to operating temperature, etc.

APPLICATION
 – For low flows of clean dry gases above their dew point, e.g., gas blending, semi-conductor industry.

COST – Medium.

An alternative instrument using a thermal sensing device below has also been developed for gas mass flow measurement.

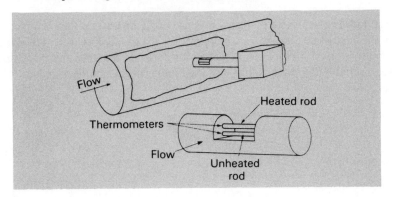

Although essentially a probe, it is also produced in a tube form for low flows. The matched platinum resistance thermometers sense the temperature difference between the heated and unheated rods. The difference is greatest at zero flows, and decreases as flow increases. Since the heat capacity of the fluid is proportional to the mass, the output will, in part, be mass flow dependent. However, in its probe form, it will be very sensitive to upstream flow profile.

A further form of thermal probe is available for flare gas flow measurements, where an instrument with a very wide flow range is

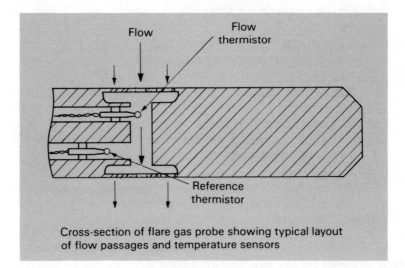

Cross-section of flare gas probe showing typical layout of flow passages and temperature sensors

required. In this device thermistors sense the temperature. One is affected by the flow while one acts as a reference for the gas temperature. Until the introduction of ultrasonic flowmeters for flare gas flow measurement, this was probably the most commonly used meter in this application.

6.3 TWIN VENTURI METER

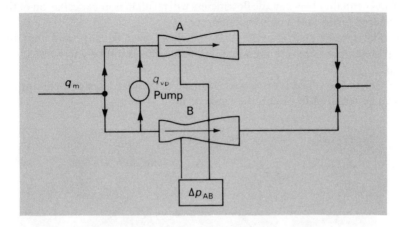

The system depends on two identical differential pressure (venturi or similar) meters in parallel, with a metering pump connecting the two lines upstream of the meters to unbalance the flows. With the pump off, the pressures at A and B should be equal. A known volume of liquid, q_{vp}, transferred by the pump from one line to the other will unbalance the pressures at A and B and, knowing the pressure difference, Δp_{AB}, and q_{vp} it is possible to obtain the mass flow rate, q_m.

TWIN VENTURI EQUATION

Pressure drop to $A = K \rho q_v^2$
where K is a constant.
If q_m splits equally, and upstream pressures are equal

$$\Delta p_{AB} = K_\rho \left\{ \left(\frac{q_m}{2\rho} + q_{vp} \right)^2 - \left(\frac{q_m}{2\rho} - q_{vp} \right) \right\}$$

$$= 2 K q_{vp} q_m$$

Thus

$$q_m = \frac{\Delta p_{AB}}{2 K q_{vp}} \qquad (6.4)$$

By introducing an imbalance and comparing the throat pressures we obtain a linear dependence between mass flow rate and pressure difference. Any inequality between the flowmeters will result in non-cancellation of the squared terms and a consequent error.

The system also assumes that the flow splits equally, and that the upstream pressures are the same. However, this is unlikely to be precisely so.

Unless the venturis are correctly made to standard designs, calibration will be required to obtain the value of K.

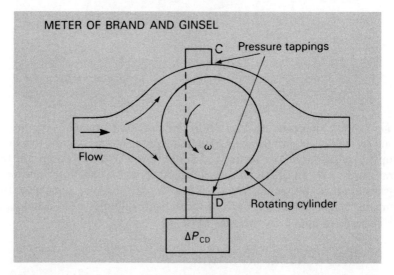

The meter shown above has similar principles to the twin venturi system. With the central cylinder stationary there are, essentially, two curved 'venturi-like' passages for the flow. Rotating the cylinder with angular velocity ω will unbalance the flows and create a pressure differential between C and D, Δp_{CD}. Since, in the absence of net mass flow through the meter, it is reasonable to assume that rotational volumetric flow will be approximately proportional to the rotational speed, it is likely that an expression similar to that for the twin venturi will apply

$$q_m = f(\Delta p_{CD}, \omega) \tag{6.5}$$

The meter is claimed to have a linear relationship between q_m and Δp_{CD}. It should also have the possibility of range changing by changing the value of ω. In this meter calibration will certainly be necessary.

PRECISION
- No information available to the author, but it is likely to be prone to error from the high values of pressure drop being cancelled, and sensitive to viscosity, temperature, etc.

INSTALLATION
- May be sensitive to ambient conditions, vibration, etc.

APPLICATION
- Claimed to be suitable for liquids or gases, but no commercial instrument is known to the author.

Little information is available on these systems, but the theory, relying as it does on the cancellation of large quantities, suggests a high sensitivity to small changes in fluid, hardware, and environment. The justification for including this instrument in this book is that the interest in mass flow measurement is such that this device may well find a market in the future.

6.4 WHEATSTONE BRIDGE MASS FLOW MEASUREMENT SYSTEMS

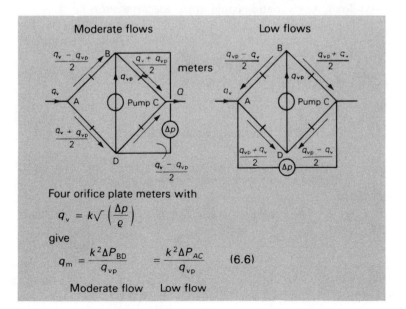

Four orifice plate meters with

$$q_v = k\sqrt{\left(\frac{\Delta p}{\varrho}\right)}$$

give

$$q_m = \frac{k^2 \Delta P_{BD}}{q_{vp}} = \frac{k^2 \Delta P_{AC}}{q_{vp}} \qquad (6.6)$$

Moderate flow   Low flow

The diagram above shows two arrangements in a 'Wheatstone Bridge' layout. Four identical flowmeters are placed in the limbs of the bridge, and Δp_{BD}, with q_v the flowrate through the pump, gives the value of q_m. To obtain the expression we use

$$\Delta p_{BD} = \Delta p_{AD} - \Delta p_{AB}$$

$$= \frac{\rho(q_v + q_{vp})^2}{4K^2} - \frac{\rho(q_v - q_{vp})^2}{4K^2}$$

$$= \frac{\rho q_v q_{vp}}{K^2} = \frac{q_m q_{vp}}{K^2}$$

$$\Delta p_{AC} = \Delta p_{AB} + \Delta p_{BC}$$

$$= \frac{-\rho(q_{vp} - q_v)^2}{4K^2} + \frac{\rho(q_{vp} + q_v)^2}{4K^2}$$

$$= \frac{\rho q_v q_{vp}}{K^2} = \frac{q_m q_{vp}}{K^2}$$

As with the calculation for the twin venturi system, a large flowrate is cancelled out. Experimentally, this will require that the limbs have precisely similar flows. Any variation could introduce large errors.

PRECISION
   – Random error probably less than ±0·5%.
RANGE TURNDOWN RATIO
   – Values quoted as high as 100:1.
ADVANTAGES
   – Suitable for fuel flow measurement.
DISADVANTAGES
   – Little experience available on effects of fluid and environmental changes, maintenance, etc.
APPLICATIONS
   – Fuel flow measurement in R & D laboratories, etc.
COST – High.

The claimed uncertainty (accuracy) of manufacturers is as high as $\pm\frac{1}{2}$ per cent of rate. Each of the system configurations was claimed to have a range of 10:1, so the flow range given above appears to stretch the combination. Environmental effects and fluid properties will possibly affect performance. A disadvantage is the lack of information on performance.

The instrument would appear to need great care and skill in operation and would, therefore, seem to be most suitable for use in research and development laboratories.

6.5 ANGULAR MOMENTUM

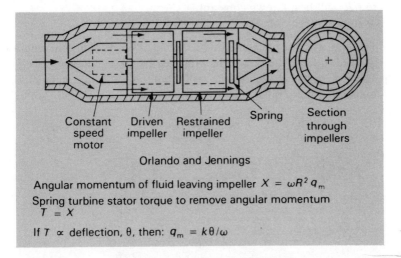

Constant speed motor   Driven impeller   Restrained impeller   Spring   Section through impellers

Orlando and Jennings

Angular momentum of fluid leaving impeller $X = \omega R^2 q_m$

Spring turbine stator torque to remove angular momentum $T = X$

If $T \propto$ deflection, θ, then: $q_m = k\theta/\omega$

A constant speed motor drives an impeller imparting swirl to the fluid. The fluid then enters the turbine which is constrained by a spring from rotating. The blades of the tethered turbine are designed to remove the swirl completely.

It can be shown from simple turbomachinery theory that the angular momentum of a fluid in an annulus is

$$X = \omega R^2 q_m$$

where we assume that a representative radius of the annulus is R and q_m is the mass flowrate. The angular velocity, ω, is known from the impeller speed. Using a long impeller with many vanes and a small annulus this should be a good approximation to the exit flow conditions. If a second similar tethered rotor removes all this swirl, and if the torque restraining this rotor obeys

$$T = s\theta$$

where s is the constant of the restraining spring, and θ is the deflection angle, then, since the torque will be equal to the angular momentum

$$q_m = \frac{s\theta}{\omega R^2} \tag{6.8}$$

where s/R^2 will be a known constant.

It is important to note the limitations of this device.

(1) The flow will not precisely follow the vanes unless sufficient length is allowed to force the flow to be axial relative to the blades.
(2) The flow profile in the annulus will modify the effective value of R.
(3) The motor speed must be known.

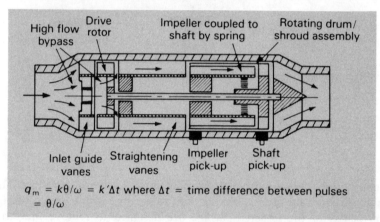

$q_m = k\theta/\omega = k'\Delta t$ where Δt = time difference between pulses
$= \theta/\omega$

Recent designs have eliminated the drive motor and use the energy of the flow to drive the rotor system. This consists of two rotors tethered together on a torque shaft. The theory of operation is more complex, but essentially the same, and the torque is measured from the lag between the two markers on the two adjacent rotors. In the meter of Orlando and Jennings, the range can be extended by changing the value of ω. Where the rotor is driven by the flow, the speed can be changed by controlling the amount of flow which passes through the driving rotor. In this way a range of nearly 50:1 is achieved.

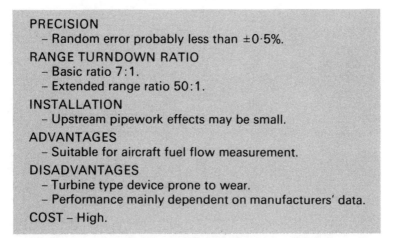

PRECISION
- Random error probably less than ±0·5%.

RANGE TURNDOWN RATIO
- Basic ratio 7:1.
- Extended range ratio 50:1.

INSTALLATION
- Upstream pipework effects may be small.

ADVANTAGES
- Suitable for aircraft fuel flow measurement.

DISADVANTAGES
- Turbine type device prone to wear.
- Performance mainly dependent on manufacturers' data.

COST - High.

Precision claims are subject to manufacturers' information, as is its susceptibility to fluid parameter changes. Although it is a 'turbine'-like meter, upstream installation effects may be small due to the modification of the flow by drive turbines, vanes, etc., but it may be more prone to wear than other types. The meter appears to be primarily aimed at the aircraft fuel flow measurement market, for which its precision and range are important attributes.

6.6 CORIOLIS EFFECT METERS

This type of flowmeter has aroused great interest in industry, and a large number of designs have appeared and are continuing to appear to meet this interest. There is always a danger with new types of meter that initial enthusiasm will be replaced by loss of confidence as the device fails to live up to initial claims. It is to be hoped that this interesting device will be the exception and will meet the increasing need in industry for a mass flowmeter. There are still areas for which it is not suitable, but with the amount of research at present these may well be reduced in the near future.

The diagrams show the various configurations of pipe used to achieve the coriolis effect on which these meters depend. The fundamental requirement is that a tube rotates while flow takes place in a radial direction. The first commercial coriolis effect meter was the Micromotion design which achieved this with a U-tube vibrating about a fixed axis so that the flow out

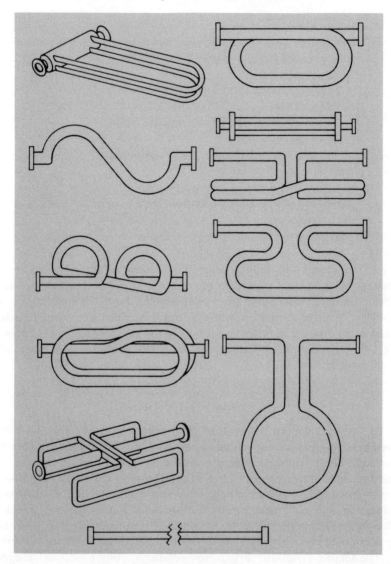

along one limb of the 'U' and back along the other, experiences equal and opposite forces twisting the tube. This is illustrated in the diagram below. Similar effects are achieved by the other designs, in each of which there must be the same features of vibration and flow.

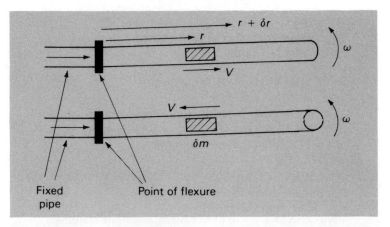

The diagram shows two pieces of pipe with angular rotation about a fixed flange. When the small mass is at radius r it experiences a lateral velocity, $r\omega$, which increases at $r + \delta r$ to $(r + \delta r)\omega$. The angular momentum of mass, δm, will change from $r^2 \delta m\omega$ to $(r + \delta r)^2 \delta m\omega$, a change of $2r\delta r\delta m\omega$, neglecting δr^2. If δm is moving at velocity V, it takes $\delta r / V$ seconds, and so the pipe will experience a force, $2\omega V\delta m$, downwards. The other tube will experience an equal and opposite force. Since the mass of the tube depends on the fluid density, $\delta m = \rho A \delta r'$, the force will be proportional to $2\omega\rho A V\delta r'$. The mass flow, $q_m = \rho A V$, and the force will be related to the mass flowrate by

$$q_m \propto \frac{F}{\omega} \tag{6.9}$$

The force results in a twist, so that the transit of the two sides of the U-tube can be related to a timed delay.

The same applies if, instead of steady angular velocity, we apply an angular vibration to each tube. The tubes will tend to lag and lead the vibration. The twist is in phase with the angular velocity, so it is a maximum as the U-tube passes centre, and is zero at the extremes of deflection of the U-tube. In most current designs two identical pipes mirror each other's vibration.

In each case a transducer (magnetic, optical, or similar) is used to sense the 'twist' or phase change. A further interesting feature is that the natural frequency of the 'U'-tube will be related to the *density* of the fluid, and may be used to obtain a value of the density.

PRECISION
Probable random error of the order of
- ±0·3% for 5:1 range.
- ±0·5% for 10:1 range.
- ±1·0% for 50:1 range.

INSTALLATION
- Claimed to be insensitive to temperature, pressure, viscosity, homogeneity, and pulsations, and, presumably, to upstream flow distortion.

ADVANTAGES
- Essentially a clear pipe bore provides a fundamental measure of mass flow.
- No rotating components.
- Available in a range of corrosion-resistant materials.
- Low maintenance.

DISADVANTAGES
- Not suitable for two-phase flow.
- Limited experience to date.
- Sensitive to vibration.
- High pressure drop at full flow in some designs.
- Some designs are bulky.

APPLICATION
- Wide range of liquids.

COST – High.

The operation of these meters depends on the fixing of the pipe to allow one part, that is, the U-tube, to vibrate, while the adjacent pipe is anchored. There is, therefore, a compromise between strength and flexibility. Some early problems may have resulted from metal fatigue, often in the presence of highly corrosive liquids. Problems such as this appear to have been overcome and are presumably avoided in current designs.

A wide range of applications are already claimed for this meter, and it is being evaluated by some industries for other applications.

One less promising application is in two-phase flows, where twin tube versions split the flow in different phase ratios and the second phase does not necessarily follow the vibration correctly.

CHAPTER 7

Probes and Tracers

7.1 PROBES

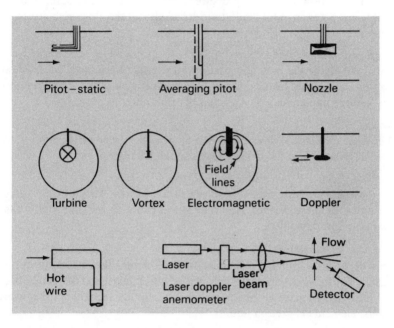

In section 1.3.2 it was shown that, for a turbulent pipe flow, a single measurement of velocity could provide a measure of the mean flow in a circular pipe. This is an option which is of interest where the cost of installing a full bore flowmeter cannot be justified. However, there is a conservatism which views the use of a single measurement with some scepticism. This is not entirely misplaced, since there are various possible errors inherent in taking only one measurement. If the probe is positioned as suggested in section 1.3.2, it is in a shear flow, and slight variations in its position or in the turbulence in the flow could affect its reading. If the probe is positioned on the pipe axis, then it will be subject to the change in profile which occurs with changing Reynolds number.

Despite these reservations, there are a range of probes available, as

129

illustrated in the box above. There is not space to discuss them in detail, but brief notes are given on each of the devices below.

Pitot tube
This was one of the earliest types, and is still used in laboratory work and in aeronautical applications. The theory is given in section 1.6.1. The kinetic head in the flow creates a pressure above the static pressure, and the difference between pitot and static head allows the flow velocity to be obtained.

Averaging pitot
This tube spans the flow and obtains an average total head based on an average determined by the position of the holes in the tube. Commercially it has various names such as Annubar, Torbar, etc.

Nozzle
A further differential device is based on a small nozzle on a probe which operates like one of the devices discussed in Chapter 4.

Turbine, Vortex, Electromagnetic, Ultrasonic doppler
All these techniques are used for local velocity probes. The turbine is one of the oldest of these devices. A paddle wheel probe at the pipe wall is also available commercially.

Hot wire anemometer
This depends on similar principles to the thermal flowmeters discussed earlier. The flow past an electrically heated wire cools it and this can be used to obtain the velocity of the flow in a gas. A similar technique using more robust elements is used in liquids.

Laser doppler anemometer
The interference between two coherent laser beams which intersect sets up a fringe pattern, and, as particles in the flow cross the fringe pattern, they reflect light with a frequency related to their velocity.

For flow measurement these techniques will usually be used in a single position probe. However, it is possible to use them to average the flow over the pipe area. In this case special positioning techniques have been developed to obtain the best average of flow in the pipe with the least number of measurement points. The use of such a technique requires considerable experience and is more suited to use by a research laboratory. It provides one method of site calibration, although the resultant uncertainty is only likely to be of the order of 1%.

7.2 TRACERS

EXAMPLES OF TRACERS

Main fluid	Tracer	Detector
Water	Sodium chloride	Electrical conductivity or sample analysis
Liquids	Dyes and chemicals	Fluorimeter, calorimeter, titration
	Temperature change	Temperature sensor
Liquids and gases	Radioactive materials	Nuclear radiation detectors
Gases	SF_6, CO_2, N_2O He, Methane	Infra-red spectrometer

One of the interesting features of flow measurement is the wide range of techniques which have been used. This is particularly true of tracer methods. They depend either on sensing a disturbance which is naturally in the flow, or on introducing one. Thus, ultrasonic doppler, correlation techniques, and laser doppler anemometry, depend on using naturally occurring disturbances or particles in the flow. The tracer methods above depend on injection of a chemical, thermal, or nuclear tracer into the flow. This can either be timed or its dilution can be measured.

In the table above are given some of the tracers which have been used, the fluids in which they have been used, and the methods of detection. Others have probably been used for specialist applications, and a particular flow may well suggest a particular method due to the particular nature of the fluid.

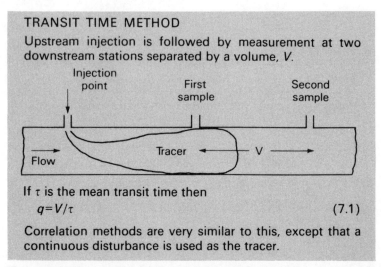

TRANSIT TIME METHOD

Upstream injection is followed by measurement at two downstream stations separated by a volume, *V.*

If τ is the mean transit time then

$$q = V/\tau \qquad (7.1)$$

Correlation methods are very similar to this, except that a continuous disturbance is used as the tracer.

The transit time method is an extension of the correlation methods, which, apart from the ultrasound sensing discussed in section 5.5.2, may use conductivity, capacitance, temperature, optical methods, and probably many other physically measurable parameters.

The concept of introducing a tracer and then timing it between two points is an obvious one. The precision of the resultant method is not so obvious, as the distribution of the tracer across the flow may not ensure that the elapsed time is that for the mean movement of the fluid.

The following methods overcome the problem of tracer distribution in pipelines where it is possible to allow time for the tracer to be completely mixed, and where it is possible to measure the concentration of the tracer in the flow. They do make the assumption that the tracer will be uniformly mixed, and there may be applications where this is not so.

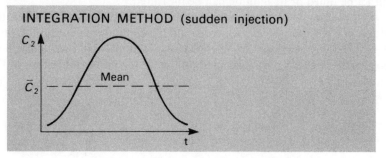

INTEGRATION METHOD (sudden injection)

Injection takes place, over short time period, of volume v m^3
with concentration $= C_1$. After adequate mixing

$$q_v = \frac{vC_1}{\int_{t_1}^{t_2}(C_2-C_0)dt} = \frac{vC_1}{\Delta t(\bar{C}_2-C_0)} \qquad (7.2)$$

knowing v, Δt, C_0, C_1, C_2.

In this method, fluid with a known concentration of tracer is injected for a short time and becomes well mixed into the main flow as it passes down the pipe. At a suitable position, the fluid is sampled for sufficient time to ensure that all the tracer has passed during the sampling period $\Delta t = t_1 - t_2$. The volumetric flow may then be obtained from the expression above, since the total amount of tracer in the main flow will be

$$q_v\Delta t(\bar{C}_2 - C_0) = vC_1$$

This method allows small quantities of tracer to be used.

CONSTANT RATE INJECTION METHOD (dilution method)

Continuity requires that

$$C_0q_v + C_1q_1 = C_2(q_v + q_1)$$

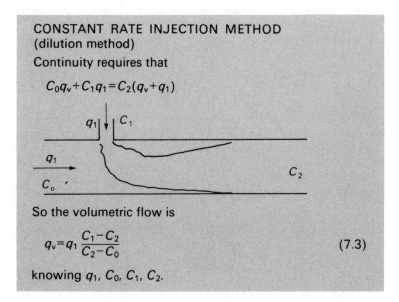

So the volumetric flow is

$$q_v = q_1\frac{C_1-C_2}{C_2-C_0} \qquad (7.3)$$

knowing q_1, C_0, C_1, C_2.

This method will allow continuous monitoring of the flow. In neither of these methods is it necessary to know the pipe size or the geometry of the pipe, but it is essential that the tracer all flows downstream, and that there are no traps or stagnant areas where tracer might collect. It is also important that the background level of the tracer concentration is a small fraction of the measured value, or otherwise the errors in measuring the concentration will become a significant fraction of the concentration difference.

7.3 CONCLUSIONS

The local velocity probes described in this chapter are generally seen as low cost, low precision alternatives to a full bore flowmeter.

The averaging pitot may offer a compromise between a full bore flow-meter and a single point velocity measurement. However, its performance and installation sensitivity may only be available from the manufacturer.

Averaging techniques making use of local velocity probes, and tracer methods may be used for site calibration. However, their use will require special expertise. The total uncertainty achievable with averaging techniques is probably, at best, of order 1 per cent, while for tracer techniques, under good conditions, it may be possible to achieve an uncertainty better than 1 per cent.

CHAPTER 8

Likely Developments in Flowmetering

NON-INTRUSIVE, NON-INVASIVE, CLAMP-ON
- The goal of instrumenting plant after construction.

OPTICAL
- Instruments which are safe in hazardous areas and not subject to electromagnetic interference.

INTELLIGENT, SMART
- Instruments capable of monitoring their own health and that of the plant.

MULTIPHASE
- The possibility of measuring oil flow at well head on the sea bed and dispensing with platforms.

This Chapter raises four particularly interesting and timely areas of development. The clamp-on instrument has, particularly, been made possible by the ultrasonic techniques under development. There is much installed plant where the instrumentation is inadequate or suspect, and where the ability to apply measurement techniques after completion or at inspection without breaking the pipe is very valuable.

The optical methods may be particularly useful in areas of high hazard where explosions are possible, and they are also unaffected by strong electromagnetic radiation.

The microprocessor offers the possibility of instruments which may store 'fingerprints' of their own and of their plant frequency spectra and, by comparison, may identify change. In addition, operating patterns may be built up from experience, and automatic comparison may allow checks on pattern changes.

The final example, of a multiphase flow measurement, is one of many, but it is a particularly valuable goal. If a satisfactory instrument could be developed to measure the flow from individual wells on the sea bed, this might allow the elimination of separators and the platforms which support them.

8.1　ULTRASONIC TECHNIQUES

NON-INTRUSIVE
- Most ultrasonic flowmeters operate with a clear bore.

CLAMP-ON
- This feature is already available for liquids and very valuable where process plant flows need to be measured without breaking the pipe.

GASES
- Most applications so far have been for liquids, but gas flowmeters are now available.

MULTIPLE SENSING/INTELLIGENT
- The possible combination of clamp-on (with wall thickness sensing), flow measurement (transit-time), profile measurement (doppler), phase slip (correlation), intelligent self-monitoring (comparison of all signals).

The interesting feature of ultrasound applied to flow measurement is the variety of measurements possible, and the combination of these measurements. Thus, wall thickness could be sensed by conventional ultrasonic techniques. The condition of the inside of the tube wall might be deducible from the quality of the reflected signal.

The noise of the ultrasonic signal may indicate turbulence level. The flow profile could probably be obtained from a range-gated doppler system and used to adjust the calibration of the transit-time system. Correlation could provide information about slip between phases while signal attenuation would indicate the amount of the second phase.

From the speed of sound it may be possible to obtain fluid temperature. From the impedance of the fluid, together with the sound speed, it should be possible to obtain density.

All of these features might be built into a master meter which would analyse pipe, flow, and fluid at a chosen installation before installation of a much more basic device automatically programmed by the master meter's dedicated microprocessor.

8.2 OPTICAL INSTRUMENTS

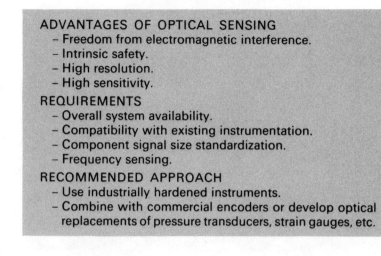

ADVANTAGES OF OPTICAL SENSING
- Freedom from electromagnetic interference.
- Intrinsic safety.
- High resolution.
- High sensitivity.

REQUIREMENTS
- Overall system availability.
- Compatibility with existing instrumentation.
- Component signal size standardization.
- Frequency sensing.

RECOMMENDED APPROACH
- Use industrially hardened instruments.
- Combine with commercial encoders or develop optical replacements of pressure transducers, strain gauges, etc.

There must be clear advantages in using optical methods, otherwise existing, well-tried methods will be more attractive. Of the advantages given above, freedom from electromagnetic interference appears to be the most important. There are certain applications where insensitivity to intense radiation, and where optical methods look particularly attractive.

The author's contention is that the initial developments of optical instruments must use existing commercial instruments well tried in industry. These should be modified to accept tried and tested optical encoders or other optical sensors. For adequate accuracy a frequency response is required avoiding the use of light intensity. For flowmeters, this implies turbine, vortex, or positive displacement meter as the likely contenders.

Industry needs to define standards for optical equipment to ensure signal and connector compatibility. In addition, overall system availability is really a pre-requisite for an optical system. thus, if optical flowmeters are being considered, then thought should be given to total optical instrumentation and control.

8.3   INTELLIGENT/SMART INSTRUMENTS

INTELLIGENT
- Sense system problems with distant micro/computer.

SMART
- Sense instrument malfunction with local micro.

FREQUENCY SPECTRUM
- Analysis of spectrum is a promising approach.

TURBINE, VORTEX, POSITIVE DISPLACEMENT
- Examine pulse train for changes or variations.

ELECTROMAGNETIC
- Analyse frequency spectrum of voltage and check with original spectrum.

ULTRASONIC
- Use both spectra from signals and also comparison between signals from various ultrasonic methods.

With increasing computing power, analysis of signal and its variation with time, etc., have become possible. Noise, which has, in the past, been rejected and smoothed out, now offers an important indication of instrument and process operation. These signal patterns may be seen as 'fingerprints' against which to compare the signal after a period of service.

Thus, analysis of the frequency spectrum of the output from turbine, vortex, and positive displacement meters may give early warning of installation changes or damage to blading, or similar.

Electromagnetic flowmeters have customarily been subject to severe signal smoothing, whereas within this signal may be information of flow conditions, presence of a second phase, flow pattern, and the like.

In ultrasonic flowmeters the possible range of information from the beam, and the possibility of sensing the agreement between the different signals, should provide information on instrument and system conditions.

There is also the possibility of totally new design concepts which benefit from the pre-supposition of the great dedicated computing power now available, and result, as a consequence, in much simpler transducers. Thus, the process may be dynamically modelled and the computer may interpret process performance from a range of parameters.

8.4 MULTIPHASE FLOW MEASUREMENT

FOR NON-CONDUCTING FLUIDS
Flow measurement by:
Venturi, target, or cross correlation, or, possibly, positive displacement.
FOR CONDUCTING FLUIDS
Volumetric flow measurement by:
Electromagnetic.
DENSITY AND PHASE COMPOSITION BY:
Impedance methods.
γ-ray methods.
Vibrating densitometer.

Several important general points need to be made about mass flow measurements in multiphase flow.

(1) The response of metering devices tends to be very sensitive to the local flow regime, which is affected not only by component mass flow rates but also by the upstream line configuration and flow history. It may, therefore, be appropriate to consider upstream flow conditioning.

(2) The best practice would be to calibrate the instrument with known phase flow rates and with an exact simulation of upstream pipework.

(3) The responses of instruments may be affected by flow transients, including both pressure fluctuations and time-dependent flow regime.

(4) When several devices are used together the instruments must be chosen such that the results of any interaction they may have with the flow does not affect the response of neighbouring instruments.

The most promising methods for measuring multiphase mass flow are to obtain volumetric flow, and to combine this measurement with that from instruments which will obtain phase distribution and density. In addition, line pressure and temperature sensors will probably be required.

Were any combination of these instruments to be used it would, of course, be necessary to redesign them to be rugged enough for the exacting conditions envisaged. This is particularly true for the important application of subsea well-head flow measurement.

A flowmeter for these applications may have an uncertainty as high as 5 per cent itself, and it is not, therefore, unreasonable to expect the system uncertainty to be twice this value.

8.5 CONCLUSIONS

One of the most interesting features of flow measurement is the number of new concepts which appear, both to improve the performance of existing flowmeters, and also in the design of new ones. This book has only been able to give a brief view of this variety. It is to be hoped that the result will allow the uninitiated reader to find his or her way to the most appropriate instrument for a particular application.

The flowmeter has been called the 'cash register' of the flow industry, measuring fluid flows worth well in excess of £bn 100 per year. Yet, whereas the accountant may work to zero error, the flowmeter engineer works with a transducer, the uncertainty of which is often not as good as ± 0.5 per cent. In selecting a flowmeter for a particular application, performance will be judged against price. However, wider justifications of good flow–measurement practice should also be considered: long-term reliability, maintenance costs, and fluid value.

In writing this book I have become particularly aware of the need in many areas of flow measurement for more data on instrument precision, on installation effects, and on long-term behaviour of instruments on site.

There is also a need for research to improve site calibration, and to develop new laboratory calibration techniques.

To the author it seems likely that we are on the threshold of a new phase of flow measurement, when the great power of the new electronic and computational techniques require a new philosophy in the design of the sensors. Most designs in use at present stem from a time when the sensor had to achieve a simply interpreted signal, because signal interpretation was expensive. Now the opposite is true, and we need to rethink our sensor design philosophy to make the most of the power of modern processing. Perhaps this book will stimulate some forward looking people to do so.

BIBLIOGRAPHY

The books and articles below, in combination with manufacturers' literature, have been of particular value to the author in writing this book and, more generally in his teaching and contract research work. It would be almost impossible to ascribe every piece of information which he has gained from them. In any case, the views are the author's gained over his years of teaching and research.

GENERAL

Flow measurement

A. T. J. Hayward, *Flowmeters. A basic guide and source book for users*, 1979 (Macmillan, Basingstoke).

R. W. Miller, *Flow Measurement Engineering Handbook*, 1983 (McGraw Hill, New York).

Guide to the Selection and Application of Flowmeters, Draft British Standard, 1987 (British Standards Institution, London).

National Engineering Laboratory Short Course Notes, *The Principles and Practice of Flow Measurement* (NEL, East Kilbride).

E. Ower and R. C. Pankhurst, *The Measurement of Air Flow*, 1966 (Pergamon Press, Oxford).

R. S. Medlock, 'The techniques of flow measurement', *Measmt and Control*, 1982, **15**, 458–463; 1983 **16**, 9–13.

A. T. J. Hayward, 'Which flowmeter for which job?', *Processing*, December 1982, pp. 35–47.

J. Hall, 'Choosing a flow monitoring device', *Instrum Control Systems*, June 1981, pp 51–59.

R. W. W. Scott (Ed), 'Developments in Flow Measurement', 1982 (Applied Science, London).

H. S. Bean (Ed), *Fluid meters; their theory and application*, 6th Edition, 1971 (American Society of Mechanical Engineers, New York).

R. C. Baker (Ed), 'Flow' (Special Issue of *Measmt Control*), 1986, **19**, No. 5.

Precision

F. C. Kinghorn, The analysis and assessment of data, in *Developments in flow measurement* (Edited by R. W. W. Scott), 1982 (Applied Science, London), Ch. 9.

A. T. J. Hayward, *Repeatability and Accuracy,* 1977 (Mechanical Engineering Publications, London).

ISO/DIS 7066 *Assessment and uncertainty in the calibration and use of flow measurement devices,* 1979.

ISO 5168 (BS 5844) *Measurement of fluid flow – estimation of uncertainty in a flowrate measurement,* 1978.

BS PD6461: Pt 1: 1985 *Vocabulary of metrology.*

Fluid Mechanics
W. J. Duncan, A. S. Thom, and **A. D. Young,** *Mechanics of Fluids,* 1970 (Edward Arnold, London).

D. S. Miller, *Internal Flow Systems,* 1978 (BHRA Fluid Engineering, Cranfield).

A. J. Ward-Smith, *Internal Fluid Flow,* 1980 (Clarendon Press, Oxford).

SPECIFIC

Differential pressure
BS 1042: Section 1.1: 1981 *Methods of measurement of fluid flow in closed conduits* (British Standards Institution, London).

ISO 5167–1980, *Measurement of fluid flow by means of orifice plates, nozzles, and venturi tubes inserted in circular cross-section conduits running full* (International Standards Organization).

L. K. Spink, *Principles and Practice of Flow Meter Engineering.* 9th Edition, 1967 (The Foxboro Company).

Sonic nozzle
ISO/TC 30/SC2 (Draft) *Measurement of gas flows by means of critical flow venturi nozzles,* January 1983.

B. T. Arnberg, C. L. Britton and **W. F. Seidl,** Discharge coefficient correlations for circular-arc venturi flowmeters at critical (sonic) flow, ASME Paper No. 73-WA/FM-8, 1973.

T. J. S. Brain and **J. Reid,** 'Primary calibrations of critical flow venturi nozzles in high-pressure gas', NEL Report No. 666, February 1980.

Positive displacement
R. C. Baker and **M. V. Morris** 'Positive displacement meters for liquids', *Trans Inst. Measmt Control,* 1985, **7,** No. 4 (July–Sept).

Turbine
R. A. Furness, 'Turbine flowmeters' in *Developments in Flow Measurement –1* 1982 (Edited by R. W. W. Scott) (Applied Science, London).

Vortex
K. J. Zanker and **T. Cousins,** 'The Performance and Design of Vortex Flowmeters', Conference on Fluid Flow Measurement in the Mid 1970s, 1977

Electromagnetic
R. C. Baker, 'Electromagnetic flowmeters', in *Developments in Flow Measurement – 1*, 1982 (Edited by R. W. W. Scott) (Applied Science, London).

J. Hemp and **M. L. Sanderson,** 'Electromagnetic Flowmeters – a State of the Art Review', International Conference on Advances in Flow Measurement Techniques, Coventry, UK, September, 1981.

J. A. Shercliff, *Electromagnetic flow-measurement*, 1987 Cambridge University Press.

Measurement of Conductive Fluid Flowrate in Closed Conduits – Method using Electromagnetic Flowmeters, ISO Technical Report ISO/TR 6817, 1980.

Ultrasonic
M. L. Sanderson and **J. Hemp,** 'Ultrasonic Flowmeters – a Review of the State of the Art', International Conference on Advances in Flow Measurement Techniques, Coventry, UK, September, 1981.

Mass
T. Gast and **R. A. Furness,** 'Mass flow measurement technology', NEL Conference, June, 1986.

P. Scanes, 'Mass Flowmeters', *Trans Soc. Inst. Tech.*, 1959, June, 119–123.

Integration methods
ISO 3385 *Measurement of clean water flow in closed conduits – velocity – area method using current-meters.*

Tracers
ISO 2975 (BS 5857) *Fluid flow in closed conduits, using tracers.*

ISO 4053 *Measurement of gas flow in conduits – Tracer methods.*

Optical instruments
G. Dickinson, 'Design considerations for optical flowmeter sensors', 2nd International Conference on Flow Measurement, BHRA, London, 1988.

Multiphase flow measurement
R. C. Baker, Measuring multiphase flow, *The Chemical Engineer*, October, 1988, pp. 39–45.

In addition to the above, further advice on flow measurement and flow measurement devices may be obtained from:

Flow Measurement Centre,
Department of Fluid Engineering and Instrumentation,
Cranfield Institute of Technology,
Cranfield, Bedford.

Flow Measurement Division,
National Engineering Laboratory,
East Kilbride, Glasgow.

Department of Energy,
Gas and Oil Measurement Branch,
Leicester.

and other laboratories which specialize in flow measurement.

Index